The Boyfriend

George Edwards

The Boyfriend
ISBN: 978-1-937250-98-0
Copyright © 2017 by George Edwards

Published by Writer's Bloc LLC

Dedication

For my children, Chad, Island, and Paige. I'm sorry for putting you through this time in my life. You have grown into amazing, wonderful people and I'm so proud and thankful to be part of your lives.

CHAPTER 1

It was May of 2007, a beautiful Memorial Day weekend. The high temperature was about 80 degrees and not a cloud could be seen in the beautiful Oklahoma sky. The sky was a beautiful shade of blue as the sun smiled down on everyone who was spending the day outside doing their favorite things. Memorial Day weekend meant spring was open! Flowers and trees were in full bloom. Lakes open for the season. Parks full of people getting out from the long winter's boredom.

My plans were to meet face-to-face with a woman who had contacted me on Yahoo Singles. We had been chatting for about a month, getting to know one another on the internet, trading e-mails and pictures since April.

Friday night I went out with my niece and a couple of her friends for dinner and drinks. When I arrived back home around midnight, I decided to check my e-mails before going to bed.

There was a message from Tammy Simmons. A long letter explaining she had broken up for good with her boyfriend and wanted to meet me the next day. She had been waiting for her boyfriend to leave permanently before asking me to meet. Sometime during the night he had packed his things and left her. Tammy said this was the green light she needed for contacting me.

I wrote Tammy a short note before going to bed telling her I would like to meet Saturday, if she had the time. Just let me know where she would like it to take place. I also told her I was sorry for not responding sooner, but I was out with my niece and some friends having dinner. From the pictures Tammy sent, she was a peach. I was excited to meet her for the first time.

Around 10 am Saturday morning Tammy contacted me, suggesting we meet at a roadside nursery not far from my house around noon. She had some errands to run before meeting me and would call when heading towards the nursery.

I was on pins and needles pacing the floor, changing clothes two or three different times, waiting for Tammy to call until finally deciding what to wear. I was as nervous as a school boy. This was my only chance to make a first impression. I planned to take my Jeep since it was so beautiful outside.

It should be perfect for meeting Tammy. Could she possibly be the next girl of my dreams? Who knows?

It was going on 2 pm, and I hadn't heard from Tammy. Many thoughts were racing through my mind. Maybe she changed her mind about meeting me. Maybe Tammy went back to her boyfriend after we talked.

Just before 2pm, my phone rang. "Hello," I said.

"Is this Jim?"

"Yes, Tammy?"

"Yes, this is Tammy. I'm so sorry for not calling sooner, but I was talking with a friend of mine, and I forgot about calling you. I'm sorry," she said with a giggle in her voice, "time just got away from me."

"Are you on your way yet?" I asked.

"I'm already here," she said. "Sorry."

"That's ok!" I said. "I'm just 15 minutes away from you. I'll be there shortly."

I hung up the phone, ran out through my garage, jumped into my Jeep and pulled out of the driveway. This was it. I was finally going to meet Tammy after a month of e-mails and pictures. Today was the day.

At last, I thought to myself as I was driving towards the nursery, I'd finally meet Tammy's voice, face-to-face. I was asking for God to watch over me, do not let me goof this up. I was so happy but nervous. Would Tammy like me? Would there be an attraction on her part, as well as mine? It works both ways when meeting someone on the internet. Their picture must pass your expectations of what you're looking for before deciding to meet. It has to be someone who you would be comfortable with in public. Tammy passed with flying colors!

I'm sitting at the stop light just below the nursery. I can see all the plants off to my right, as it sits on top of a little hill. I took a right at the lights. As I got closer, I could see Tammy standing alone, in the middle of all the plants. Not another soul was there. I pulled into the parking lot to get a closer look. I could see her standing there looking down at a row of plants, waiting patiently for me to walk over to say hello.

"This is it!" I said aloud to myself, jumping out of my jeep and walking over to where Tammy was standing. Just be yourself, I kept thinking. I wanted to hurdle as many plants as I could to cut down on the walk time. Looking at Tammy from behind, she looked like Jennifer Anniston standing there. I had a good feeling about this!

I made my way through the maze of plants over to where Tammy was standing. She was looking down at some Morning Glories. I stood there waiting for Tammy to look up at me.

She slowly looked up at me. "Aren't those just beautiful?"

"Oh my God," I thought to myself, gazing into her beautiful green eyes. She's beautiful, my brain whispered. I had to tell her what I thought of her.

Looking into her eyes, I felt they were the most beautiful thing I had ever seen. I was dumbfounded. At that moment the sun encircled her with a glow of beauty. She stood around 5'5", with shoulder-length blonde hair, green eyes matched her knee-length olive-colored shorts and a smile which could only have come from an angel.

"Hello, I'm Jim." Smiling, I stuck out my hand. I wanted to touch her hand.

"Hello, I'm Tammy. Finally, we get to meet…face-to-face."

"Yes, we do," I said, not taking my eyes off hers.

We talked a bit as we slowly made our way back to the parking lot, smiling at each other the whole way.

Jackpot! I was thinking to myself. Tammy was perfect!

We were standing in the parking lot next to my jeep, and I noticed Tammy was looking around like she was waiting for someone else or avoiding having to look at me.

"What are you looking for?" I asked.

"Sometimes my old boyfriend would follow me places," she said.

At that time I really didn't think much of it, I was busy running things through my mind if she likes me or not? What is she thinking right now?

"Do you know where a post office is?" she asked, "I need to mail some letters."

"Yes, I do. I can look out my back yard and see the post office. It's just down the road a couple of miles," I said.

"Can I follow you there?" She asked.

"Yes, of course you can. Turn left at the lights and follow me."

The trip to the post office was nerve racking. I still hadn't received a signal yet if Tammy was interested in me. I was pretty good at reading people, but she had me stumped. I kept my eyes on the rear-view mirror to see if she was going to ditch me by turning off on a side street. Tammy followed me right into the driveway of the Post Office. I pulled forward so she could mail her things.

Tammy pulled up beside me. She asked if I would like to stop and buy a six pack of beer and maybe drive to the park and talk some more.

"I don't like beer," I said, "but I'd like a Jack and Coke. How about we go to a little Irish pub right up the street from my house? We can get a table in the back so we can talk and not be bothered?"

"Ok let's go!" She said.

Tammy followed me to the pub, parking beside my jeep. We walked inside where we found a table in the back out of all the noise from the patrons playing pool and watching baseball on the big screen television. We ordered a couple of drinks. I wanted to know everything about her, leaving nothing out and without distractions.

"Where were you born?" I asked.

"Sioux City, Iowa." she said

A big smile came upon my face. An Iowa girl, I thought to myself.

"I was also born in Iowa," I said, "Fort Dodge, Iowa. You and I were born only a few miles apart. Isn't that funny? Here we are in Oklahoma, just a few miles apart again."

"So, when is your birthday?" I asked.

"December 4th, 1960," she said.

"I was born September 30th, 1960," I said.

We sat there telling each other our stories of the past and present. I couldn't believe I was sitting with such a beautiful woman, who I could hardly take my eyes off of, even for a second. I could see Tammy was just as excited about being here with me. Yet she was a little nervous, I suppose from meeting me for the first time. I can honestly say we never had an uncomfortable silent moment people have when they meet for the first time. Running out of things to say was not us, we were both excited to tell our stories to each other.

Tammy said she had been to her father's grave just a month ago. She asked him to bring someone good into her life. "When I saw your picture on Yahoo Singles in February, I thought to myself you looked like a little shit. I actually wondered if I would be able to handle you."

We laughed a bit over her comment about me. I am a little shit, but in a good way.

"What's your father's name?" I asked.

"Jim Jones. My parents were from Steamboat Springs, Iowa. They adopted my sister and me when we were little," she said.

I was looking at Tammy with a surprised look on my face.

"What's wrong?" She asked.

"This is too weird!" I said.

"What's weird?" She asked.

"When I was a boy growing up in Iowa, my junior high and high school girlfriend's name was Tammy Fokken. Her dad's name was George Fokken. Tammy and I were so much in love. We wanted to get married one day. She was the perfect girlfriend. We had so much in common. Tammy's father was a truck driver and had taken a new job in Conroe, Texas back in 1978. George, her father, told me before leaving Iowa, to give them a couple of weeks to get settled into their new place, and then Tammy would call me. I could move to Texas, find a job while waiting until Tammy graduated from High School, and then get married."

"So, what happened? Did you guys ever get married?" She asked.

"No, it never happened. When Tammy called the house, my mother answered the phone. She told Tammy I had found someone else. I asked my mother every day for a month if Tammy had called. My mother would say no, not today."

"Why would your mom do that?" She asked.

"I'm not sure. I guess mom didn't want me moving away from her. For years it ate at me. Then one day I needed to hear it from her. I got Tammy's number from information and made the call. When Tammy answered the phone, I had a frog in my throat. I knew it was her voice on the other end and I started to hang up. But instead of hanging up, I just came out and asked her what happened? Why didn't she call me? Tammy was upset and started crying. She told me she had called every day, but my mother told her I had found someone else. We both had a good cry over the phone that night, both of us crying over what might have been.

"Tammy told me she had met someone in school her senior year and they were dating. We hung up after talking for about an hour. I waited for over a year for that phone call before finally giving up. I apologized to Tammy for my mother's actions. I have no idea, why my mother would do that to me."

"I had been with Tammy for five years. From the time I was thirteen years old, I always knew we'd be together forever. My heart has been broken for many years because I never got the chance to marry my true love. Meeting you makes me wonder if God is giving me a second chance with my Tammy from Iowa."

"What do you mean a second chance?" She asked.

"Well you both have the same first names, both your fathers' names are Jim. You both have the same blonde hair, green eyes, same height, and beautiful smile. Who knows what God's plans are for us after tonight? I've never gotten over what might have been if I'd gotten that call."

"I was adopted because my real mother didn't want me." she said.

"I bet this was not the reason your mother gave you up, Tammy."

"My mother had more kids after giving me up for adoption. I didn't find out who she was until I was twenty years old and I had siblings, brothers and sisters. Why would she more have kids after giving me up?"

"I suppose it was timing, Tammy, just not the right time! But she loves you and probably regrets it now. I bet she wonders all the time if she did the right thing. Back then things were different for a single pregnant woman. Only she knows the real story of why she gave you up."

I'm thinking to myself why would Tammy make being adopted sound so bad? Her adopted parents did such a great job with her and her sister from what Tammy has told me. Did she want me to feel sorry for her? Was she was feeling like a misfit in society? Did she think I wouldn't date someone who was adopted?

"Tammy, what are you looking for in a man? That is, if you're in the market for a good man right now?" I asked.

She looked at me thoughtfully, "I'm looking for a good Catholic man. A man with good family values, someone who loves kids, animals, with a job and a home of his own. You had it all in your profile, which is why I contacted you. I need someone good in my life. I'm tired of fighting with Billy all the time. I'm glad Billy took his things and left. Maybe he'll find someone else and leave me alone."

So far so good. I met all those qualities Tammy was looking for in a man. I hope Billy finds someone else too, so Tammy can make room for me in her life.

"What about you? She asked. "What kind of woman are you looking for?"

"I'm sitting across from her right now!" I said, looking to score some points.

I nailed it! Tammy was smiling and blushing at the same time. I could tell from her actions my answer was perfect, just what she wanted to hear from me. She was all smiles adjusting herself in her chair. I was waiting for the hair flip most goofy blondes do when a man compliments them.

I had my best flirting clothes on and wasn't about to pass up the chance of trying to sweep Tammy off her feet. I felt like this was too good to be true. Never in my wildest dreams did I think someone as beautiful as Tammy would be searching for a man on the internet. With her looks, she could have anyone she wanted.

"Let's go out for a bite to eat," I said. "I'm starved. I haven't eaten since breakfast."

"What should I do with my car, leave it here?" she asked.

"I only live two minutes from here. You can park in my driveway. I'm going to put my jeep in the garage, so go ahead and park behind me."

"Good, I wanted to see where you lived anyway," she said.

CHAPTER 2

My House

Tammy followed me down the street to my house, pulling into the driveway behind me. I opened the garage door to park my jeep inside. Tammy was walking up the driveway when she saw my Harleys sitting in the garage and commented on how nice my bikes were.

"Would you like to take the bike out to eat?" I asked.

"Sure, it's a beautiful night for a ride, I would like that." She said.

I invited Tammy inside to see my house. She took one step inside my house then stepped back out into the garage, a scared look on her face.

"What's wrong Tammy?" I asked.

"You're married!" Tammy said as she stood in the doorway to the garage looking confused and scared for some reason.

"I'm not married! Why would you think that?" I asked.

"Your house was too clean for a single man to live alone. There are no cigarette butts in the ash trays, no empty beer cans lying around," she said.

I chuckled at Tammy. "I don't like beer, remember? Plus, I like a clean house! Now come in please." I grabbed her hand, pulling her into my kitchen. Tammy walked slowly through my house looking at all my furniture, pictures and plants which were neatly placed in my home.

"Your table is set. Why is your table set?" she asked.

"I always have two plates and silverware with glasses upside down on my table," I explained. "When I'm finished eating my meal, I wash my dishes and set them back on the table. Now let me show you the upstairs so I can get you a sweatshirt to wear on the bike."

Tammy followed me upstairs we entered my master bedroom. I had a beautiful cherry sleigh bed covered with a white duck feathered comforter, with different colored throw pillows for decoration, along with a matching dresser and nightstand.

"I love your bedroom. Did you paint it this color?" she asked.

"Do you like the color?" I asked.

"I love that color of green. Almost matches the shorts I have on," she said.

In the guest bedroom down the hall, I had an old antique iron bed I had picked up at an antique shop in Collinsville, Oklahoma. I love walking the sidewalks in small towns, shopping for old things to bring home and restore back to its natural beauty.

"I just love old furniture," she said. "Your bed reminds me of my grandmother's house when I was a child. I love old squeaky iron beds."

Tammy loved the tour through my house. She was smiling as she went from one room to another. She loved my four-foot angel picture which hung on the wall as you climbed the stairs to the second story.

"Wow!" Tammy exclaimed. "You have a beautiful home. It's so warm and well decorated for a man. You have great taste Jim."

Made me wonder what kind of men she dated. Why was she so surprised to walk into a clean house and assume I was married only because it was clean?

"Let's take the bike down to Peoria Street, and we'll eat at Crow's Creek bar and grill. I'm really hungry Tammy, let's go."

"Billy has a bike too," she said. "I'm not sure what kind it is, but it is a Harley. Billy's bike is not as big as the one you have. It doesn't have a radio or a nice padded seat with an armrest like yours does."

Crow's Creek is a little bar and grill which sat on Peoria along with other biker bars in the area. It was never too crowded. This night we sat out on the patio where we could hear the band playing inside while watching the other bikes rolling up and down the street revving up their motors and showing off their bikes.

I think every town has a Peoria. It's one long street full of shops and fine restaurants. A great place to shop during the day or cruise the streets on your motorcycle or hot rod in the evening hours when the heat of the day is over. Some people just like to walk the sidewalks and window shop, while others enjoy the company of their spouse as they walk hand-in-hand under the dimly lit sidewalks after dark.

Tammy and I sat out on the patio and ordered catfish dinners along with a couple of beers. Maybe it was the company, or maybe the relaxing atmosphere, but that night I didn't seem to mind the taste of beer. After eating what we could, we sat and shared small chit chat. I wanted so badly to kiss Tammy, but I didn't want to rush into things with her. She had brought Billy's name up a few times today since we met; maybe she was not done with Billy. Maybe it was just a fight, and they'll be back together tomorrow, or maybe Tammy just needs time with someone different to make her choice. Break ups are hard. I'll give her all the time she needs. I'm not going to get my hopes up just yet.

After we finished our dinner, we sat enjoying the music for a bit. I wanted to take the highway home so Tammy could lean back on the bike and enjoy the cool evening air blowing through her hair.

But instead of leaning back, Tammy leaned forward wrapping her arms tightly around me and resting her chin on my shoulder. I felt like the king of the world. A warm sensation took over my body the feel of her holding me, it was all I wanted from the first time I met her. For some strange reason, I knew Tammy felt comfortable with me tonight and things were going to be ok from that moment on.

Back at my house, standing in the living room, I asked Tammy if she would like to watch a movie. "Or do you need to go home?" I asked. "It's after midnight; can you stay a little longer?"

"I'd love to watch a movie," she smiled. "What do you have?"

"How about Pulp Fiction?" I asked.

"I like that movie."

Pulp Fiction was one of my favorite movies too. Anything written by Quentin Tarantino was worth watching. We sat back in my big overstuffed chair holding hands. Tammy leaned over and pecked me on the lips, a shy smile playing across her lips. "Today was the best day I've had in a long time," she said, snuggling closer to me and laying her head on my shoulder.

I was hoping the night would never end.

About half way through the movie Tammy got up and sat on the floor facing me. She started mumbling a bunch of scattered details on how she kicked Billy out because he was doing drugs and cheating on her with her friends.

"Billy spends a lot of time at Sidelines Bar," she said. "That's probably where he is tonight. Every Friday and Saturday night Billy is there until closing time."

While Tammy was telling me this stuff, she was all fidgety on my floor, doing some stretching, sit-ups, looking down, not looking me in the eyes. She looked nervous for some reason. My first thought was maybe she had too much to drink, or maybe she was having second thoughts about breaking up with Billy?

Maybe she missed Billy? Maybe she felt it was wrong being here with me so soon? I'm just sitting back in my chair wondering what the hell she was doing. Was she trying to tell me something? Did she have something to say, but just couldn't come out and say it? Was I supposed to fill in the gaps in her story?

"Billy is mean to my dog, Roxie. She hates him." She said.

This went on for an hour and a half. I'm trying to listen for any clues. Just one word from Tammy which would help me figure out what she was trying to say to me. It was like listening to a two-year-old, catching only one word out of the sentence and trying to figure out what it is they want!

I finally had to stop her mid-sentence, "I'm tired Tammy, it's almost 3 in the morning. You are more than welcome to stay the night up in my room, and I can sleep here on the couch, but I'm exhausted. I never stay up this late. I haven't seen midnight in a long time."

Tammy decided to stay the night. I walked her up to my room and told her to get one of my t-shirts to sleep in. If she needed me, I'd be downstairs on the couch. I kissed her on the cheek before walking back down to my couch.

Lying on the couch while this beautiful woman was upstairs in my room was too good to be true. I knew that I'd get to see her again in the morning; giving me another chance to win her over. That night I went to sleep with a smile on my face while thinking to Tammy would forget all about Billy if we had another day like we had today. Tomorrow was a new day.

Sunday morning, the second day of Memorial Day weekend, I woke up about 8 am, jumping off the couch with the same smile I went to sleep with. I folded my blankets and started the coffee. Pachelbel was playing softly throughout the house. I knew Tammy would feel like she was in heaven waking up to the music playing. I sat out front on my porch sipping on my coffee and having a smoke, waiting with anticipation to see Tammy once again. I was hoping we could spend the whole day together.

I wasn't so sure of Tammy's plans, or if she even told me about her plans. I couldn't help running things through my mind. What was she trying to say about Billy last night? None of it made much sense, other than her dog not liking Billy because he was mean to it. Did they break up because of her dog? Who cares what the reason is; Tammy is here with me now. I wanted to be her new boyfriend.

Tammy walked out to the front porch around 10 am with a cup of coffee in her hand.

"That is the most beautiful music I've ever heard," she said.

"How did you sleep, pretty lady?" I asked.

"Oh my God, I haven't slept so well in a long time. I can't remember when I slept this soundly all night. I just loved your bed. It was so comfortable," she gushed.

"Good, I was wondering if we were going to be able to spend the day together. Do you need to run home to check on your children?" I asked.

Tammy said," My kids are with their dad at the lake for the weekend."

Music to my ears, I thought to myself.

"They won't be home until Monday, so you have me until 5 pm tomorrow afternoon," she said. "I've never done this before."

"Done what?" I asked.

Tammy said, "I've never spent the night at a man's house who I had just met. Don't think badly of me."

"I don't think anything. It was too late for you to drive home safely."

"I'm glad you understand."

We sat out on the front porch sipping on some coffee. Tammy started telling me a little more about Billy. "Billy packed some of his things and left my house Friday night. He went back to his house. That's when I could get a hold of you. I'm so tired of him lying to me. I know he's on drugs, but I can't prove it right now. He spends nights and weekends in jail for a stunt he pulled at my house last year. He had cheated with one of my friends on their way to a concert in Oklahoma City. She told me about it. That's when I told Billy we were over. I was tired of his lying to me and cheating all the time. He showed up at my house one morning with a gun and tells me 'tonight is the night, Tammy. It is going to end here.' If I broke up with him, he was going to kill himself.

"I called the police, and they arrested him. He received six month's probation on a work release program, only because I loaned him $10,000.00 for a lawyer to prevent him from going to prison. He promised me he'd go to counseling, but he hasn't gone. The police took all his guns and his license to carry. If he's caught with a gun, he goes to prison."

Tammy took another sip of coffee before continuing. "They let Billy out at six in the morning to go to work, and he has to be back by ten that night. I'd go up to the jail on weekends to visit him. All he would do is bitch about being in there. I told him he was lucky he wasn't in prison and to stop his bitching and just be glad he only has six month's probation. I know he blames me for him being in there. I really think Billy needs counseling to help him with his drug abuse and anger towards me, and everyone else."

After listening to her story, I wasn't sure what to think anymore. Telling someone you are going to kill yourself is just a way of manipulating a person to get your way, like a child holding their breath for that cookie.

"Look, Tammy, if you're still seeing Billy, or you need time to get completely away from this guy, I'll be right here. I don't want to be in the middle of your break-up with him, and to be honest, I don't need any drama in my life right now."

"Billy and I are done for good. Tomorrow when I get home, I'm going to take the rest of his things over to his friend's house. Then I'm going to change the locks on my house so that he won't have a key anymore."

When she looked me in the eyes and assured me she was done with Billy, I could see the sincerity in her, and I believed her. However, Billy showing up with a gun bothered me.

"Enough about Billy," I said. "Let's go out and grab some breakfast."

"Can I take a shower first?" she asked.

"Not a problem. Do you have other clothes to wear?"

"I'll wear what I was wearing yesterday," she said. "I'll stop by my house to get some clothes after we eat breakfast. I want to show you where I live."

After Tammy's shower, we climbed into my Jeep, and I took her to Mimi's restaurant for some breakfast. Mimi's was a nice quiet place, offering friendly service and great food. Tammy and I sat in a booth across from one another so I could look into her eyes while we talked. I've always believed that someone who doesn't look into your eyes while talking is hiding something.

"Not that I want to spend the day by talking about Billy," I said hesitantly, "but the gun thing with Billy concerns me. My nephew was shot in the head in February by a stray bullet fired from some kid in a crowd. It hit him in the temple. He's still recovering in the hospital. My sister thought he was going to die. Even the doctors weren't sure if they could save him. They had to put him into a coma to help the swelling go down on his brain just so they could remove the bullet. That's why I hate guns. They scare me. Bullets have no eyes, and people are crazy nowadays. They think hiding behind a gun will solve their problems. Do you think Billy would ever use a gun on someone?"

"I don't think so," she said. "Billy hunts deer. Sometimes he will carry a gun in the back of his pants to make him look tough. But like I said, he's not allowed to carry a gun anymore. Now he tries to scare people with his 'wolf look.' He thinks if he stares at them with his 'wolf look' they won't bother him. I've never seen Billy in a fight. He would probably lose if he were ever in a fight."

CHAPTER 3

Tammy's House

After breakfast, Tammy wanted to show me where she lived. She needed to get some different clothes to wear. Tammy had me drive in the back way to her neighborhood, just in case Billy's truck was there. Tammy lived in a little suburb outside of Tulsa, called Broken Arrow. A nice neighborhood with manicured lawns and well-kept up houses covered by big oak trees out front. We turned on Fredericksburg Street. Tammy told me to drive slowly so she could look for Billy's truck.

"Stop right here Jim!" she said.

I was looking for Tammy's driveway to pull into. We were stopped in the street in front of a house. "Is this where you live?" I asked.

"No!" She pointed up the street to a house. "That's where I live, but stay here for now, I'm looking to see if Billy's truck is in my driveway."

We sat there for quite some time with Tammy looking up the street at her house. She had a serious look about her. You could see her mind was racing. I'm not sure what was going through Tammy's mind as she looked up the street at her house. I could see Tammy was really thinking things over in her head, about going home to get some clothes; her face was giving it away. She looked frightened, as if she was going to steal someone's newspaper in broad daylight. We sat there for a few minutes longer, her taking small breaths from time to time.

"Tammy! What are you afraid of? It's your house! If Billy is there, tell him to leave, or call the police. Come on, let's get you some clothes." I said.

"Oh no, Billy would be pissed if he saw you with me," she said. "You don't understand. If Billy is there, he has a way of talking me into staying with him and having sex. I'm done with Billy. The best way to handle this is not seeing him at all. I'll finish packing his things when I get home then drop them off while he's at work. Maybe Billy will find someone else and go away. Let's go, Jim. If I need to, I'll buy something new to wear."

When we left, I was puzzled at what Tammy just told me about Billy. I wanted to hear more stories about Billy, what he might do to her. Why did Billy have such control over Tammy? I understand breakups are hard. Was it Tammy who could not let go, or was it Billy refusing to let her go? Maybe they were married, and Tammy didn't tell me the truth? Something is not right about their relationship; only a married woman would be afraid to go with another man.

CHAPTER 4

Riverside Drive

We took a drive down to Riverside Drive Park, a stretch of park about 10 miles long which ran alongside the river. The City had spent a lot of money to bring people out to enjoy things like frisbee golf, jogging trails, roller skating, bike riding, and a splash pad for the kids; or you could just sit in the sun, reading a good book. They had a walk bridge crossing the river with offsets for people to fish, or sit enjoying the scenery. It was full of people today.

Tammy and I sat under the sun in the green grass, watching people enjoy the day with family and friends. New lovers were walking hand-in-hand, while parents were riding their bikes with their baby on their back enjoying the sights of the park. Dogs were catching frisbee's, while joggers were listening to the music from their Sony Walkmans.

"Tammy, tell me more about yourself?"

Tammy asked, "What would you like to know?"

I asked, "Do you work?"

Tammy said, "Yes, I work for Met Life, the big building right off Hwy. 51. I sit in a cubicle all day, talking on the phone with customers. It's a boring job but pays the bills. I could do my job from home, if they let me."

"Tell me about your children?"

Tammy said, "I have two girls and a boy, whom I love very much.

"My oldest child, Linda, has her psychology degree. She works for Shadow Mountain Institute. Linda works with troubled kids who have anger problems which started from home or drugs. Linda doesn't like Billy very much, because of the way he treats me.

"Linda has been helping me with everything since my divorce from Edward, like paying my bills and stuff. Linda has run off a lot of guys I've dated, because she didn't like them. Linda will like you. I'm sure of it" she said.

"Steven, my son, is the middle child. Edward has always gotten on Steven's case because Steven was not good enough in sports. That made Steven angry inside; he has quite the bad temper. I've tried to help him with it, but Steven just yells at me. You'll see when you come to my house how mad Steven gets. I had to tell Steven to go live with his father because of his anger. I'm not a bad mother; Steven is just out of control with his yelling and hitting things.

"Lori is my baby girl; she is so carefree. Nothing bothers Lori, she really has great friends, and she is doing so well in school too. I'm so proud of Lori; she has handled our divorce well. Lori lives with me, she hangs out in her bedroom, or with her friends most of the time. I have two dogs; Roxie she is a Boxer—the one who hates Billy, he's so mean to her. Tori is a Miniature Doberman. I also have three cats and an African Grey Parrot."

"My you have a lot of pets," I said. "I gave my dog away to the neighbor kids. Wilson would always run down to their house and play with the boys, until their mother brought him back home. Wilson and the boys would whimper, so I asked if they would like to have him.

Their mother said the boys could have him, so I packed his food and cage, I said my goodbye's and off they went."

Tammy and I left the park, and we headed back to my house. I told Tammy I would like to cook dinner for her tonight.

"I have a better idea," she said, "how about we cook together? So, what are we cooking Jim?" She asked with a laugh.

I told Tammy we were going to cook my favorite chicken pasta, with broccoli, spinach, shrimp, and Texas garlic toast; served out on the patio.

Tammy said, "Sounds delicious. Can we stop at the liquor store so that I can get some wine for dinner?"

After stopping off for some wine, Tammy and I went back at the house. We started cooking together, flirting with each other the whole time. Tammy seemed comfortable in my house with me. We'd slow dance from the music I had playing, with some innocent touching, while cooking dinner.

I sat across from Tammy, while we ate dinner. She was so beautiful, I found myself daydreaming. How perfect my life would be if we could do this every night together.

After we finished eating, Tammy helped with the dishes, so I could reset my table. After the dishes had been done, we wandered out to the back patio. Tammy sipped on some wine. I had a Jack and Coke, which I only drank on special occasions, as this was one of them.

While sitting on the patio, Tammy set her feet on my lap to get comfortable. We talked more about her past growing up. I started rubbing Tammy's feet, trying to get her more comfortable, she was always fidgety. I wanted to know why her marriage failed? I won't get answers if I don't ask questions.

I wanted to know more about Tammy, asking questions was one way of getting to know, who Tammy really was. Even if she left things out of her stories, I could fill in the gaps, deciding for myself if she was telling the truth, or hiding something from me. There's always two sides to every story, his and hers, and right and wrong.

CHAPTER 5

Tammy's Divorce

I asked, "Tammy what happen with your marriage to Edward?"

"Edward had an affair with an 18 yr old friend of the family. We had some friends over for a cookout. Edward went missing, so I went looking for him. I looked out the kitchen window, and I saw Edward having sex with the girl on the trampoline."

"Ouch," I said.

"I freaked out and went running after the girl, but Edward kept me from getting to her," she said.

"I took her keys, and her CD's out of her car. I found her cell phone. I kept all those things; I wouldn't give them back. She had to buy another cell phone," Tammy said, laughing.

"Tammy, why would you take her things?" I asked, "When your husband was the one married to you. He was the one hurting you, not her. This had to be going on for quite some time? It just doesn't happen overnight, and you had no clue."

"I hate her. She broke up my family," she said. "After being adopted as a child, being given up by my mother, I didn't want to be alone again, without a family."

"Tammy, you make being adopted sound like the worst thing that could ever happen. You and your sister are very lucky Jim and Mary adopted you, raised you in a normal home, and gave you the love you needed."

"I know I love my parents. I'm very thankful for everything they had given me," she said.

"Tammy, your husband broke up your family. Apparently, there was already trouble if he strayed out back where you could catch him. I understand you are upset about the whole ordeal, and on how it happened. Edward has every right to see whoever he wants to, as long as he is happy, and she is good to your children. You shouldn't make your children choose between the two of you. It isn't a matter of who is right or who is wrong in a divorce."

Tammy said, "I didn't want to lose my marriage, or it to end. Edward is still seeing her. I hate her for breaking up my family. I won't let my kids go around her. I had a nervous breakdown after that. I had to take family leave for six months from work. My doctor put me on Valium to keep me from going crazy. Linda had to take care of things, because I just lay in my bed and cried for weeks."

I said "Tammy, once again, you shouldn't make your children choose between the two of you. It isn't a matter of who is right, or who is wrong. They have to deal with your divorce, in their own way. They love you and their father, so don't make them choose.

"Tammy, I never told my children why I left their mother, that story is mine to keep even though they saw some of it. I never ask them to choose me as the good parent. I just told them we grew apart, and I decided to call it quits. So, if I'm the bad guy in our marriage, in my children's eyes, I am ok with that."

I asked, "Tammy is that when you met Billy, after your divorce from Edward?"

Tammy said, "I have known Billy since we went to Nathan Hale High School together. Billy and Edward were best friends all the way through high school, and stayed friends even after. I was Edward's girlfriend at the time. Billy always wore buckskin boots, he had long hair. He walked around like he was real tough, but he wasn't tough at all. His brother Mike would beat up people for Billy. Billy would always start fights, and let Mike finish them.

"Even when we were all married, we would get our families together to go camping, and have cookouts together. We'd go out drinking as couples. We were all good friends. When Billy and his wife divorced because she found another man, Edward was there for Billy to help him through it. After I caught Edward, I wanted Edward to leave, but he wouldn't. So, I asked Billy to tell Edward to move out so I could get on with my life. After a few months of Billy being here for me, things just happened one night, the next thing I know we were together."

Tammy said, "Billy has always had a crush on me. Even in high school, he carried a picture of me in his wallet when I was 16 years old dating Edward. Billy still has it. Billy told me he has always loved me, even when I was married to Edward. One night we were all out drinking at a bar, Edward got up to use the restroom. Billy pulled out the picture of me he had in his wallet. He showed me the picture and told me he loved me. I looked at Billy and asked 'What did you say?' Billy said, 'I have always loved you, Tammy.' I looked at Billy, reminding him I'm married to Edward, his best friend. Billy then said he meant he loved this picture of me."

I said, "Wow, your husband's best friend is carrying his wife's picture around in his wallet. That's kind of weird. Then he tells you he loves you while your husband is in the rest-room? I bet Billy was happy to ask Edward to leave. Now was his chance to have you, not just your picture, but the girl in the picture."

Tammy said, "Yeah, I guess so. I didn't plan on doing anything with Billy, it just happened one night when he was over for a visit. We had a few drinks. Sitting on my couch Billy leaned over and kissed me, and then things took off from there."

It was dark out, and the bugs were starting to bother us on the patio, so we moved inside. Just in time too.

Tammy's phone started to ring. It hadn't rung since we'd been together.

CHAPTER 6

The Phone Call

Tammy said, "It's Linda, my daughter," as she looked at her phone.

Of course, I was going to listen to what Tammy was saying. Since her children were with their dad and his girlfriend at the lake, Tammy was talking to Linda, her oldest daughter. Linda had asked Tammy if she minded if they go to their dad's house for a cookout after returning from the lake tomorrow.

Tammy said, "That's fine, just keep Lori away from that bitch! I don't want her talking to Lori."

Tammy was very rude and mean with her words to Linda about her ex-husband's girlfriend. Tammy didn't want her children liking their dad's girlfriend. Surprise, a side of Tammy I haven't seen up in until now. I guess everyone has three sides to them; The Good, The Bad and The Ugly. I couldn't wait for Tammy to hang up the phone, but she kept on the same subject, Lori, talking to Edward's girlfriend. Tammy's name for her was "the bitch."

Then Tammy told Linda she was staying at a friend's house for the weekend because she needed to get away for a while. But Tammy wouldn't tell Linda who the friend was she was staying with in case Linda tried calling her friend to check on her mother.

When Tammy finally hung up the phone, she started explaining the conversation she was having with Linda. Of course, I heard the conversation; I could fill in the details. It wasn't hard to figure out who the bitch was.

Tammy said with some anger in her voice, "I don't want that home wrecker talking to Lori. They are going to Edward's for a cookout tomorrow after they get back from the lake. I told Linda to keep Lori of away from that bitch!"

I said, "Tammy, maybe I don't have the right to say anything."

But she was bringing it to my attention. I had to speak up on the situation and tell her my thoughts, as one parent to another.

"Tammy, I think you were wrong in saying what you did to your daughter. Your ex-husband has every right to be happy with whoever he chooses, just as you have the same right. I can see you are trying to make your children choose sides in this. You've been divorced for quite some time from Edward now. You've had relationships with other men, mainly Billy, Edward's best friend, for how long now?

"Yet you are still trying to make Edward's life miserable by using your children against him. You will never be happy with anyone, until you can let this anger go you hold inside of you. You will always be competing with the new girlfriend. You haven't been able to break them up after all this time, let it go and be happy for them stop using your children as a bargaining tool.

"Someday your kids will have children of their own. You will have to share your grandchildren with Edward and his girlfriend or wife, if they ever get married. She will be at weddings, graduations and birthday parties. So, you need to get ready and start feeling differently about them as a couple, or you will be left out in the cold."

Maybe I hit a nerve, but Tammy just stood there. She listened to me explain my thoughts on her situation. Tammy never interrupted on what I had to say. Being a divorced dad too, surely Tammy understood where I was coming from. So, either she would leave, or she would stay, it was her choice.

"Tammy, as a father it would kill me to the core if my ex-wife was using my kids against me."

Tammy didn't leave that night, nor was she mad at me after what I'd said to her. We spent the night sleeping on my couch in the living room after watching a movie. It was nice just holding her throughout the night. However, I was worried about snoring into her ear, but I took my chances. I just wanted to be with her. It didn't matter what we were doing as long as we were doing it together.

CHAPTER 7

Breakfast with Paige

Monday morning. Memorial Day. Our last day together before Tammy went home from our wonderful three-day weekend.

Tammy and I decided we would go out for breakfast after we showered. I did some laundry the night before. I washed Tammy's clothes, so she had something clean to put on after showering. She has been wearing the same outfit for three days now. She was afraid of going home because Billy might be there.

My youngest daughter, Paige, met Tammy and me for breakfast. I introduced Paige to Tammy, and they seem to hit it off really well. I taught my children to have good manners as they grew up. Always be nice to people, unless they give you a reason not to be. I wasn't worried about Paige not liking Tammy since they just met. When Tammy got up to use the restroom, I knew Paige would ask a few questions about Tammy.

Paige was my youngest of three kids. Paige stood about 5' 3" with golden brown shoulder length hair, and dark brown eyes she received from her mother. Paige kept me busy when she was younger, keeping the boys away from the house.

"Tammy is pretty dad, where did you meet her?" she asked.

I couldn't tell Paige I met Tammy online. I wanted to tell her something romantic or daring, like I rescued Tammy from a burning house or saved Tammy from a speeding car as she was crossing the street. But I had nothing!

"I met Tammy at a nursery," I said. "The other day shopping for a plant to put in my kitchen. I saw Tammy standing alone in the middle of the nursery looking at all the beautiful flowers. I thought she was absolutely beautiful herself, I said hello and here we are today, having breakfast."

"That's cool dad. Tammy seems really nice. What are you guys doing after you eat?"

"I think we are going to walk the mall for a bit. Would you like to come with us?"

"I would love to dad, but I need to get back home, and finishing cleaning."

"Thank you for meeting us for breakfast Paige. I gave her a hug as she left the restaurant."

Tammy said goodbye to Paige as she left, heading back to her house. Tammy and I drove across the street to the mall. We walked the mall, doing a little window shopping, while still getting to know one another better. We didn't hold hands like new couples do after meeting, which I thought was kind of strange at the time. But maybe we weren't there yet in our friendship, I didn't expect anything from Tammy, until she was ready to take it to the next step.

Maybe Tammy just needed to get away from Billy for a while to figure if he was worth keeping by spending time with me. I can only guess what is going through her mind at this point. I've only had one kiss, on our first night together. Tammy just seemed so uptight when we were out in public; she was always watching her back. I don't think Tammy really noticed I was watching everything she did from the time I met her.

CHAPTER 8

Ex-Boyfriend Billy

Later that afternoon back at my house we were sitting out front on the porch to break away from the sun which was beating down on the patio out back.

Tammy said, "Billy was probably at my house all weekend waiting for me. He will be pissed not knowing where I was all weekend. I hope he didn't hurt my animals.

I asked Tammy, "Would Billy do that?"

Tammy said, "I never know what Billy will do to hurt me when he doesn't have control of me, or he doesn't know where I am. This is the longest I have been away from Billy since being together. He will be pissed, but I don't care. I hope Billy finds someone else soon and goes away for good."

"Tammy, I don't want any drama, or be in the middle of any fights with you and Billy," I said. "I don't wanna be the reason you are leaving him. You leave Billy for your reasons. Don't use me, please. If you go home today and decide to get back with Billy, please tell me. Don't lead me on. I don't want to share you with Billy or anyone else."

"Billy packed his things for the last time," she said. "When I get home I'm packing the rest of his things and taking them to his friend's house. Then I'm going to Lowe's to buy some new locks for my house. I'll call you later tonight after I do that and let you know how things went. I can assure you, Jim, Billy and I are done for good. Getting away from Billy this weekend was the most relaxing weekend I've had in a long time. This is what I want in my life. I don't wanna follow Billy's rules anymore."

I figured I wouldn't receive a call from Tammy. She'll probably get back together with Billy, and I'll never hear from her again.

"Would you like to see me again?" I asked.

"Of course, every chance I get, silly," she said.

I walked Tammy to her car; she pecked me on the lips and smiled as she drove off.

I didn't expect to hear from Tammy again; she was too scared of Billy. Afraid to leave him. Maybe she was still in love with him. Maybe Tammy was at a crossroad in their relationship. If Billy was anything like most men, when it's break up time, we are done, no calls or emails. Unless Billy was like the few crazy men who won't let go.

I deleted her number; I'm done! I don't like the drama, and it's a waste of my time and energy. I'm not a jealous or controlling person; I'll not beg for someone to stay with me. I'm not going to get my hopes up until Tammy calls, if she does.

Later that night around 8 pm Tammy called me.

Tammy said, "Billy had shown up at my house, during the afternoon sometime. While Lori was upstairs in her room changing clothes for the cookout at her dad's house, Billy just walked into my house. Then Billy walked upstairs to Lori's room, and he opened the door while she was standing in her panties and bra."

"Billy asked Lori, 'Where's your mother?' Lori told Billy she didn't know where I was. She said she'd been at the lake all weekend with her dad. Billy said, 'I haven't seen Tammy all weekend,' then he walked out, slamming the door.

"I'm pissed that Billy just walked into Lori's room while she was in her undergarments.

"I packed Billy's things and took them to his friend's house. I told him to tell Billy that I changed the locks and not to come back."

Tammy said, laughing, "My friend Penny and I changed the locks on my house. It took us a long time because we had no idea how to do it."

I felt better. Tammy was serious. She was done with Billy. I was getting a chance to love again. I figured Billy would be like any other man; when it's over take your losses and move on. Maybe Tammy was right; maybe Billy would find someone else and leave her alone.

So, for the next two weeks, Tammy came to my house right after work, and we hung out until 9 pm. Each time she would pull up into my driveway, she would be wearing a little sundress with flip flops, running up the driveway jumping into my arms, wrapping her legs around me. Tammy would say with a smile, "I missed you today" and gave me a kiss. I just loved her greetings. I was so happy; I was hoping Tammy shared the same happiness I felt inside. Tammy was amazing; I was so thankful God brought her into my life.

Tammy and I spent most nights just enjoying each other's company, sitting out back on my patio, sharing the day's events, or anything new which might have happened during the day while we were apart. We always hung out on my patio, or just snuggling on my big couch. There was never a dull moment when we were together; Tammy was so full of energy, always happy to see me at the end of her day.

Most nights I'd cook dinner for us. Tammy loved my cooking. We'd do the dishes together after dinner, growing closer together as the days went by. We never called one another during our working hours. We waited until after work, by then we were ready to be together again.

Tammy told me Billy tried calling her numerous times during the day at work.

Tammy said, "I didn't answer Billy's calls. I don't want to talk to him. Billy would try talking me into taking him back. If Billy shows up at my house, I won't answer the door, because if I let him in, he will talk me into having sex with him and taking him back."

I said "Tammy, Billy telling you he would kill you is his way of controlling you. It's a scare tactic to keep you around."

I asked "Tammy, how does someone talk you into having sex with them when you're done with them? It just doesn't make sense to me."

Tammy said, "You don't know Billy. He is a real smooth talker. Billy has that way about him. Billy can get any girl he wants, once he gets to talk to them. I don't think Billy would kill me, even though he said he would, if I break up with him again."

I had to ask Tammy if Billy good looking, a sexy GQ man? "I don't get it, Tammy. How does Billy have that kind of control over you? You've told me Billy lies and cheats on you with your friends."

Tammy said, "Billy isn't good looking. He is almost bald and has skinny arms. It's just Billy has a way of talking women into having sex with him."

"I can see I'm not getting anywhere with this Tammy," I said, "but if you decide to see Billy again or have any sexual contact with him, let me know. Please don't keep secrets from me. I'll find out if you're lying to me. I don't tolerate any lying, big or small, from anyone. I'm asking you be to honest with me always. I'm a good man worth keeping. You'll figure that out soon enough."

Tammy said, "You have nothing to worry about, Jim. I'm not going to see Billy anymore. I really like you a lot; I want to see where this will go. We have so much in common. We have so much fun together too. I've been looking for a man like you for a long time. I just want Billy to go away and leave me alone."

CHAPTER 9

The Ugly side of Tammy

Tammy was coming over to my house right after work. Playing her head-banging music quite loud with her car windows down and her sunroof open, I could hear Tammy coming from a block away as I sat out front on my porch waiting for her. Tammy pulled into my driveway with her music blasting. I waited until she got out of her car and I received my greeting, which I loved so much.

"Tammy, please turn the music down when driving on my street. My neighbors might not like it so loud."

Tammy said, "Fuck your neighbors. If they don't like it, don't listen to it."

Wow! I didn't see that coming. I have seen the good, the bad, now I've just seen the ugly in Tammy.

I said with a firm tone in my voice, "No, Tammy, not 'fuck my neighbors.' Please keep it down when coming into my neighborhood, that's all I ask.

"Tammy, I also noticed you were driving while drinking a 32-ounce mug of wine. Do you need to drink so much wine at one time?"

Tammy said, "It helps me calm down and unwind after work. Besides, there is nothing wrong with having a glass of wine after work."

I said, "You're right about that. I heard it was healthy for a person to have a glass of wine every day, but not a whole box of wine at one time. Do you always drink that much?"

Tammy asked, "Does it bother you? "

"I wanted to be sure it was your true feelings, running up to me, jumping into my arms, and not the wine talking," I said.

"My father was quite the drinker. He always used his drinking as a crutch for his wrong doings. He hurt a lot of people, including me. So yes, I guess maybe it does bother me to a point. I've always been afraid of people who drink—you just never know what they might do or say to hurt you."

"I'm sorry," she said. "I'll slow down on my wine drinking when I'm around you, Jim. And to answer your question, my true feeling about you makes me do what I do when I see you. I miss you so much while I'm at work."

Tammy came to my house every day after work for a couple of weeks. She wasn't hearing much from Billy, only a few calls and some voice mails on her phone. Tammy was sure Billy had found someone else and moved on for good. I felt better now that Billy backed off. This was my chance to win Tammy's heart and become her new boyfriend.

CHAPTER 10

Tammy's House

Tammy invited me to her house so I could see how she lived. She is always talking about her flowers and plants she loved so much. Tammy told me she had some 30 year old Hosta's a friend gave her. She said they had planted them out front of her home together. Tammy said she planted some moonflowers out back which were 6 feet tall I'd have to see. She said, "They open up at night, and close during the daytime."

I told Tammy I would love to come by your house to see all your plants and meet her children.

Tammy met me in her driveway with her everyday greeting; jump, hug, and kiss.

Tammy said, "Come in," holding on to my hand leading me into her house for the first time. I was greeted by her parrot who yelled "Hello!" as soon as the door opened. I answered hello back. I thought it was pretty cool, a bird greeting you as you came in the front door. You'll always know when the front door is opened up, that's good security.

We entered the front door into Tammy's living room with a stairway to the left leading to the second story. It had a window half way up looking out onto the driveway, lighting up the stairway during the daytime. The sides of Tammy's couch and chair, which sat in her the living room, were shredded from her cats sharpening their claws.

That's why I don't like cats, I thought to myself, getting past the torn furniture. Tammy continued the tour of her home taking me into the kitchen, then to her computer room. It was in a dark corner of her house with no windows, just a ceiling fan for light. The last stop on the first floor was the master bedroom. Tammy had a huge bed that took up most of the bedroom. I could see it was full of trash under her bed. It smelled like animal urine. The carpet had a thick black trail of dirt leading through her bedroom into her master bathroom.

The master bathroom had a little glazed window so you couldn't see in or out of it, letting a little light in during the day. The master closet was off to the right as you entered the bathroom, it was full of boxes and stuff.

I always pay close attention to every exit when I enter a new place in case of a fire or some other emergency. I made mental notes of everything about Tammy's house.

Tammy took me upstairs. She told me before going up the carpet was pulled up in the hallway because of her dogs crapping and urinating on the carpet. Tammy said it smelled bad, but not to pay attention to it.

Tammy was right; it did smell bad. It was dark and dirty in the hallway. Tammy opened the door to Linda's old bedroom, and it was full of stuff everywhere.

Tammy said, "Linda hasn't gotten all of her things out yet. She has been slowly moving."

Tammy opened Lori's bedroom door. It was very clean and smelled like a young girl's room should. Even her bed was made up.

Tammy really didn't want me to look inside Steven's room, but she did open the door. It was trashed out with holes in his walls and a closet door broken off hinges with holes in it. It looked like a bomb went off in his room.

I just shook my head. I said, "My kids would never do that to my house." I shut the door as I walked back down stairs with Tammy.

Tammy had a beautiful home, but the living conditions inside were bad. The first thing I would do is get rid of the animals. Give them away to someone who could train them not to use the house as their personal bathroom. Have the cats declawed, and buy new furniture.

Tammy took me outside of her home. She was so proud of her plants, naming each one and telling me the story behind it. She should have been born a bee because she went from plant to plant smelling each one, taking in a deep breath from the scents of each flower. I could see she belonged at a nursery with as much as she knew about each plant. Out back through a door in Tammy's garage she had a table where she would stand for hours potting or repotting her plants. It wasn't much of a table, just some legs with plywood nailed to the top. She told me Billy had made it for her so she could spend time outside doing what she loved.

What really caught my attention was the area outside the garage door enclosed by an 8-foot privacy fence. No one could see what was going on in that little corner of her yard. Her 6-foot moonflowers covered the area beside the door that led into the garage. I thought to myself, *If anyone wanted to break into her home, they would jump the fence kick in the door that led into the garage.* There wasn't a dead bolt on that door, either, making it easy to open with a driver's license. There was just something about that area that didn't seem right; it concerned me.

In today's world, you always need a dead bolt on every door, especially the garage door at the far end of the house, surrounded by a fence and tall plants that hid everything in that area.

Off in an area close to the fence, Tammy told me Billy had planted a little garden of tomatoes, and bell peppers. There was a few growing, just about ready to pick.

I made many mental notes of Tammy's house that day just in case I needed to get out of trouble started from Billy. We grabbed a couple lawn chairs and sat in the garage opening to keep out of the hot sun. Tammy had her jug of wine, while I sipped on a bottle of water.

Tammy said, "My girls should be here anytime; I want them to meet you."

"What if they don't like me?" I asked. I was really referring to Linda.

Tammy said, "they will like you. They are good girls. They have wanted me to get away from Billy for a long time now and find someone good to me. So they'll be happy I met you. Linda will be the hardest one, but in time she will like you."

CHAPTER 11

Meeting Linda

A car pulled into the driveway. Out of it came Tammy's daughters. We just sat there in the lawn chairs as they walked up to where we were sitting. Tammy introduced me to the girls.

"Linda and Lori, this is my new friend Jim."

Linda stood about 5'6" and about 135 pounds, with blonde hair down to the middle of her back. Being the only one in her family to receive a degree, Linda acted as if she was above everyone else, having a piece of paper from a technical college and stating she was smarter than everyone else. I could also see it in the way she was looking at me.

"Hello, Linda, nice to meet you," I said. She was scanning me hard. Linda was standing there looking deep into my soul with nothing but a stare and a straight face. It was like she was smelling shit or something. Not even a crack of a smile. Linda said "Hi" with a straight face and a nod from her head.

She walked into the house through the garage door, like the warden of a prison. Oh boy, I thought to myself, she's not going to be very friendly. I'm going to have to kiss her ass to be able to see her mother. And to top it off, Tammy told me, Linda has run a lot of men off. I wondered if I was next.

Lori was a pretty teenage girl, standing about 5' 5" with sandy brown straight hair hanging down to the middle of her back. She had a pretty smile. Lori said hello with a smile as she followed Linda into the house.

I was looking over at Tammy. I said, "That went over like a turd in a punch bowl. I don't think Linda approves of me. She kept staring at me like I was a criminal or something. Is this how she always acts around other men?"

"Linda is just protecting me. That's just who she is. In time she will like you."

How much time will I have to serve in Linda's prison before she likes me, I wondered? I know these kinds of women; always making men walk on eggshells, waiting for her approval of them.

"Steven is the one that will be hard to get along with," she said. "It took a long time before Billy and Steven got along. Steven doesn't think anyone is good enough for his mother."

"All boys think that," I said. Something else to worry about. Linda, Steven, and Billy.

Things started to get better as time went on. Tammy said her girls thought I was good looking.

That was good news; I started going over to Tammy's house every night after work around 6 pm. I hung out until 10 pm before heading back to my house.

CHAPTER 12

God's Little Joke

Saturday the weather called for partly cloudy skies. We had a date to shop for plants for the flower bed at my house. May in Oklahoma was bad about pop up storms any time of the day. But there was more sun then clouds that morning, so I decided to drive my Jeep over to pick up Tammy. She really enjoys riding in my Jeep without the top on and the music blasting.

We were going to spend the day together, walking around Lowe's in the garden section. Spring puts the planting bug in everyone. Tammy had some ideas of what to plant in my little flower bed out front of my house.

I arrived at Tammy's house around 10 am that morning. I rang the doorbell a couple of times with no answer. She must be sleeping or in the shower. I noticed her front lawn needed mowing, so I walked around to the shed in her back yard, I pushed her mower around to the front yard, I started cutting her grass. I figured she would wake up hearing the mower going, but she didn't.

I kept mowing, around to the back yard, close to her bedroom window. The blinds came up, there Tammy was standing with a big smile on her face as she stood there looking at me cutting her grass. She came out of the back door, to greet me with a hug and a kiss.

Tammy asked, "What are you doing?"

"I'm cutting your grass, you boob. It's 10:30 am. Why are you still sleeping?"

Tammy said, "I always sleep late on weekends."

"We have a date to run to Lowe's to find some plants for my flowerbed, remember?"

Tammy said, "I need to shower first; give me a few minutes."

"Ok, you shower, I'll finish mowing the back yard."

We backed out of her driveway sometime around 11:30, heading toward Lowe's, which was only three miles away. I noticed the sky was getting darker as we were driving, I could smell the rain in the air.

If you don't think God has a sense of humor and enjoys a laugh every now and then, keep reading.

While we were at a stoplight not far from Lowe's, I had a feeling the rain was close. I swear, the minute the light turned green it poured buckets on us. It was raining so hard I couldn't see the road in front of me.

My glasses were wet, along with my windshield. My wipers going as fast as they could, but not fast enough. Tammy was leaning back in her seat with her arms spread out laughing and screaming like she was on the log ride at the fair. She loved it! We were soaked to the bone, the rain was cold, and the air from driving my Jeep without the top on was cold too.

If it were any other woman with me that day, she would have been pissed, yelling and cussing at me for not having the top on my Jeep. But not Tammy; she seemed so happy, always up for anything fun. She made the best out of a bad situation. That's what I loved about her.

It felt as if the black cloud followed us for the next mile and a half. The thunder was God laughing at me. I had to drive with my head sticking out of the Jeep so I could see the road. I was even getting splashed from passing cars.

I passed by Lowe's and went straight to my house another mile down the road to dry off. One block from my house the sun was smiling down. Everything was dry, except us.

We were still laughing as we jumped out of the Jeep running into my house, then upstairs to my bedroom. In my room we started taking off our cold, wet clothes, laughing with blue lips and runny noses from the cold rain. I grabbed Tammy a towel to wrap up in. I put on boxers so I could run downstairs to put our wet clothes into the dryer.

I ran back upstairs. I was still cold. Tammy was sitting on my bed waiting. With one long leap, I jumped tackling her on the bed, and we rolled around laughing. I was laying on top of her, our smiles dimmed, her eyes sparkled. Tammy opened her towel. She said, "Let me warm you up."

That was our first time making love. It was incredible! I just wanted to spend all day looking into her eyes as I laid on the bed with her, touching her body. Moments like this seem to go by so fast when everything seems so perfect.

After sex, my status changed from my Friend Jim to my Boyfriend Jim. Being the boyfriend now, meant that I was upgraded in status. Being upgraded came with "I love you" more often, I would have to meet Tammy's parents, friends, and buy her gifts on special occasions. There's a lot more pressure being the boyfriend now. I'd be around more, and I'd have to put up with Tammy's children's crap too. When you love someone, it all seems worth it.

Things were much better between Tammy and me after making love. We were able to let our inner feelings out toward each other. The hard part of our relationship was over for us. I call it breaking the ice, and sex was the first step of any new relationship. Everything was in place now! I was Tammy's new boyfriend, and things would only get better from here. Or would they?

We put on our warm, dry clothes fresh out of the dryer and decided to stop to grab lunch before going to Lowe's to finish what we started out to do this morning. Tammy picked out some plants for my flower bed. I left them in the Jeep, while I hung out with Tammy that afternoon at her house relaxing in lawn chairs, under the Bradford pear tree which decorated her front lawn.

CHAPTER 13

Devonna at the Spirit Fair

I had mentioned to Tammy about the Tulsa Spirit Fair coming next weekend. "I have a card reader, Devonna, who has been reading for me many years now."

"I have heard of those people who read cards, but I have never been to one. What do these people look like Gypsies?" she asked.

Laughing, I said, "No, this is not a room filled with old women Gypsies and their crystal balls. They are people like you and me; they have a gift from God who delivers messages to us through them. The room is full of healers, readers, vendors selling books, cards, and aura pictures showing you what colors surround your body."

Devonna Gilpatrick was a kind-hearted woman with short red hair and a beautiful smile. She had been a nurse at the Veterans Hospital in Oklahoma City for many years while doing her readings on the side to help others. Devonna always told me "Jim, if I were just ten years younger I would snatch you up." Devonna had a gift from God. She was able to deliver messages to everyone who was lost in the moment and to be comforted with answers.

Of course, Devonna couldn't tell you if you were going to die or pick the winning numbers for the lottery. She was there to help you with your marriage, money, work and love. Throughout the many readings I've received from Devonna, she's covered all those areas more than once. Who doesn't want to know about a raise coming, or a new love entering your life soon?

I've known Devonna for about fifteen years. She has always been as sharp as a tack when it comes to reading my cards. I was having some trouble with my marriage, I needed some answers. Devonna was right on the money then, she's been reading my cards ever since. Devonna has been my earth angel, delivering messages to me.

"I would love to go and find out what's going to happen with us," Tammy said. "I'm going to ask Devonna about Billy too. I hope she says Billy will find someone new and leave us alone."

"Devonna will tell you the truth. She will not cover up anything to spare your feelings. I would like to hear what she has to say about Billy too, for my own comfort, and peace of mind," I said.

That next weekend Tammy and I went to the Spirit Fair. We walked around while waiting for our appointment with Devonna, killing time, looking what the vendors had to sell. Waiting with anticipation for our readings, I wondered what Devonna had to say about Tammy and I being together. My mind was filled with good thoughts about Tammy. I was hoping for nothing but good blessings, that Tammy was a good person, the right girl for me. Devonna gives it straight! Good or bad, she'll not sugar coat things, or only tell you what you want to hear. Some people don't believe in spiritual readers, but I know the Angels have messages for me. They've delivered many times over the years.

We stood across from Robert Baca, who was talking to a woman delivering messages from her loved ones who had crossed over. Robert stopped and looked at me for a second, then he turned away started talking to her again. Then he held his hand up to her stopping for a second.

Robert Baca was well known for being able to talk with people who have crossed over to their next life. I've seen Robert on television many times. He was good, and this was my first time seeing him in person.

Robert got up from his chair, walked over to me, and said, "Your brother thanks you for the roses. He wouldn't leave me alone until I gave you that message."

An instant chill came over me; I was hoping my brother would show up to say hello. I loved my brother, who died from cancer at the age of thirty years old. Greg loved roses. I put them on his casket as I said my goodbyes to my brother. Greg was ornery his whole life. I knew if Greg were here he'd bug Robert until his message was delivered to me.

I sat down at the table with Devonna after giving her my usual hug. She shuffled her cards, laid them down one at a time on the table, looking at each one closely.

"Jim, so far things with Tammy would just be fine," she said.

According to Devonna Tammy and I knew each other from our previous lives. Tammy was royalty, and I was a guard during that time watching over her. Being just a guard, I wasn't allowed to speak with her. But I was very much in love with Tammy then.

"Now you have found each other in this life. Your relationship with Tammy is too new right now for me to see further down the road. That's all I can tell you at this time," she said

Then Devonna asked if I had been finding coins in strange places.

I said, "Yes I have. How did you know that?"

Devonna said "Your Mother is leaving you dimes in odd places, to let you know she is with you, Jim. Some people who have died leave coins for family members to find to let them know they are with them."

Devonna knew I was finding dimes, at least one a day. This blew my mind.

Tammy sat down after my reading to get one of her own with Devonna. I walked around a bit while Tammy received her reading. I returned before Tammy asked about Billy. I wanted to be there to hear what Devonna had to say. Maybe I could get some insight on who he was as a person.

Devonna laid out Billy's cards. She had a strange look on her face as she laid each card out.

"Without hesitation, this man is a sexual deviant," Devonna said.

I looked at Tammy to see the surprise on her face, but she just kept looking at Devonna and had no facial expressions at all, like this was no surprise to her. She wanted to hear more about Billy.

Devonna said, "Billy is an evil man; he is a very mean person. I see Billy will go to prison for a long time. For what I don't know. He will be in prison by November of this year. I also see a pair of legs, not working, like someone is in deep water trying to tread, but their legs won't work. I don't know what any of this means, it's just what the cards are telling me about Billy right now."

Wow, I thought to myself, that was some reading! Devonna didn't tell me to be careful or watch out for Billy. Was Tammy telling me the truth about Billy? She just sat there not saying a word, or asking any questions. I think Tammy knew the answers already, she didn't have to ask.

Tammy and I talked about what Devonna said about Billy as we walked out to my Jeep. Tammy couldn't figure out what Devonna meant about a pair of legs not working. It had me stumped too, but I didn't know Billy at all. I wondered what Billy would do that was so bad to get a prison sentence for a long time. Devonna didn't say Billy was a violent man, just a mean person inside. I could breathe easy. He wasn't going to try and hurt me, or Tammy. Being a sexual deviant, I understand what Tammy was talking about that if she were to see Billy again, he would talk her into having sex with him. That's what deviant's do.

We left the Spirit Fair, and I drove us up the street to a parking lot with a pay phone. I wanted to call my sister, telling her what Greg, our brother, had said to me. I opened the door to my jeep and right there was a shiny new dime. I picked it up, showing it to Tammy, then I looked up and thanked my Mother for being around me that day.

It's funny how my Mother just leaves dimes places before I get there for me to find. It's like she knows where I'll be going that day before I leave the house. I wonder though if her dimes are warnings to keep alert, or just letting me know she is there with me always.

CHAPTER 14

Billy's First Prank

One night after dark out around 9 pm, Tammy and I were sitting on her couch watching The Dog Whisperer on television. Tammy believed this man could really talk to dogs. Crazy, I know. The doorbell rang. Tammy looked over at me. with a startled look on her face.

Tammy said, "I bet that's Billy," as she got up and walked slowly to answer the door.

Oh crap, I thought to myself, unsure what to do at this point. Do I sit here or get up and stand at the door with Tammy? I started thinking of the exits in her house just in case I needed to get out. Would Billy be a jealous boyfriend, filled with rage, or not? Would Billy push the door open wanting to fight? I just sat there on the edge of the couch, staring at the door while Tammy opened it. Then she stepped outside, and I'm wondering what's going on. If Billy is out there, would Tammy tell him I'm her new boyfriend now, to go away and leave her alone?

Then Tammy walked back in with a confused look on her face.

"There's no one out there," she said. "I bet that was Billy ringing the doorbell then hiding."

Tammy no sooner finished her sentence, when the doorbell rang again. This time I ran up the stairs to look out the window, which looked out into the driveway, to see if someone was out there playing games.

This is not cool, I was thinking to myself. It's giving me the creeps, it's dark outside. I'm inside her house, not in control right now, not sure what to do at this point. I couldn't show Tammy any fear, so I just walked back downstairs and sat on the couch. I could see Tammy's face was full of thoughts. She had her fingers over her mouth thinking as she walked back to the couch.

As she closed the front door again Tammy said, "Billy is doing this stuff; he is such a chicken shit. He'll do stupid things like this, thinking I'll break up with you and go running back to him. After a while, Billy will stop, and maybe he will find someone new at Sidelines and forget about me."

"What is Sidelines?" I asked. I don't go to bars, so I had no idea what Sidelines was, or where it was, in Tulsa.

"It's a bar down on 57th and Lewis," she said. "Billy is always there. Everyone there knows Billy. The bartender, Cricket, knows Billy and I very well. Whenever Billy's favorite band plays there, we'd go out to dance and drink. Billy's there almost every night after work."

"I thought you said Billy was in jail on weekends— thought he had to be back by 10 pm?"

"He does," she said, "that's why he is not ringing the doorbell anymore tonight. Billy doesn't want to be late getting back to jail. See it's 9:45. Billy has only fifteen minutes to get back to the jail. Sometimes Billy would tell them he is working overtime, then he stays out until the bar closes at 2 am."

"How does he pull that off? They don't smell alcohol on him when he returns? Do they not check with his work schedule about overtime hours? Billy can just say I'm working over tonight, and not go back until he wants to? Where does Billy work, Tammy?"

Tammy said, "Billy has a friend who tells them Billy works part time for him. He gets Billy out all night sometimes. Billy had come here before and spent the night with me, telling them he is working overtime. He works at Sun Oil in West Tulsa by the railroad tracks."

I asked, "So Billy just works the system, breaks the rules as long as he tells them he is working? And they just let him do as he pleases, and it's ok with you that Billy does this?"

Tammy just looked at me; she was speechless.

"Well, Tammy it's 10:00 pm, I need to get home. I'll see you tomorrow after work."

I couldn't help but look around every step I took as I was walking to my truck. I was wondering if Billy would come out of a dark corner and confront me. I was still shaken up over the doorbell ringing with no one being there. Billy must be one of those guys who acts like a child when someone breaks up with him.

Sure, ringing the doorbell was harmless, if that's all he is going to do for a while until he finds someone new. I can live with that. Maybe Billy is too afraid to confront me. Maybe he is a chicken like Tammy said. I'll just forget about it until it happens again—if it does ever happen again.

CHAPTER 15

Trip to Iowa

Every year I return to Iowa for the Freedom Rally. It's a big biker rally every Fourth of July, where hundreds of people attend for a weekend of motorcycles, music, food, camping, and friends.

I told Tammy I was going to the rally with my brother Shaun. My best friend Shawn Laplante was also going. I'd be loading up the bikes in my trailer taking off early the morning of July 3rd. Tammy was invited to join us if she wanted to go.

Tammy said, "Billy and I have been to some rallies here in Oklahoma." She said they had been to Pawhuska Rally a week before she had contacted me. "We had a lot of fun until Billy started his shit, and we started fighting. But I'll see if I can get off work. I will let you know, as soon as I know something."

I haven't been to the rally in Pawhuska Oklahoma since 1983. I received my Harley wings tattoo back then. The rally was dirty and rough; it hasn't changed at all, so I've heard. Not a good rally to take a nice woman to for a weekend getaway.

Tammy called me two days before I was leaving. Tammy said she could get the time off work and wanted to go if it was still ok for her to join us. "I haven't seen Iowa in many years, I'd love to visit Iowa again. I asked a friend of mine to feed my animals and water my plants while I'm gone. Lori is staying with a friend. So I'm ready for a getaway. What time are we leaving?"

I told Tammy 8 am and no later, because we had tattoo appointments at 6 pm.

Every year Permanent Ink sets up a time for us at 6 pm to get some new work done. It's an eight-hour drive depending on the weather and traffic, and I like spending time with my sister before we unload the bikes at her house. Then we'll ride into town to get our tattoos done.

Tammy arrived that morning about 7:45; my truck and trailer were already loaded with our things. When she arrived, I grabbed her bag of clothes and locked up the trailer. Off we headed to Iowa for three days of motorcycle vacation. My buddy Shawn LaPlante and my brother Shaun sat in the back seat of my truck while Tammy sat up front with me. We talked about whatever came into our minds just to pass the time away. We even all sang together after hearing a song we all knew. Believe me, none of us could have made a living singing.

We rolled into my sister's driveway about 5 pm, just in the nick of time. I had been holding gas in my stomach for about 200 miles, I needed relief. Everyone got out of the truck, while my sister and her husband Gary walked out to greet us. I walked in front of my truck, I let loose the hours of gas I had been holding. Ahh relief, I thought to myself as my swollen stomach shrunk back to its normal size.

Tammy turned, looked at me and asked, "Was that you?" She started laughing, as did everyone. I tried to blame it on thunder, but there wasn't a cloud in the sky.

Yeah, my first embarrassing moment with my new girlfriend; I knew it would happen sooner or later. Thankfully, it was forgotten as we unloaded the bikes. We left our camping stuff on the truck until tomorrow morning.

We could visit with my sister for about thirty minutes before heading into town to get our tattoos done.

Permanent Ink Tattoo Parlor always greeted us with a handshake and a "hello Oklahoma." They always asked, "How was the trip up?" The owner would always ask me about my daughter, Island. He had given her a tattoo one year when she took a trip up with dad. So, we paired off with our artists, telling them what we wanted this year.

Mine was a back piece, a tree with twisted branches reaching out, one you would find in a Halloween movie. Nothing scary, just spooky looking. I had a wizard, dragon, and castle on my back; the tree would be a perfect addition.

Everyone took their seats and start getting their ink work done. I was sitting backward on a chair so the artist could do my back. I was facing my best friend Shawn Laplante who was getting his work done by Joe. My brother was having his done by the owner of the shop. Tammy was standing next to me, watching the artist outline my tree. Tammy was taking pictures of everyone's work being done so we'd have photos of the trip. After an hour into my tree tattoo, I was sitting there in pain that I was trying to hide from the others.

I heard Tammy blurt out, "You do great work! I just love you."

I lifted my head to see who Tammy is talking to. She was standing over my best friend, Shawn, talking to the artist, Joe, who was doing his tattoo.

"I just love you!" she said a couple more times.

By this time, I could see Joe was getting turned on by what Tammy was saying. His face was turning red. Joe really thought Tammy loved him. Hell, Tammy hadn't even told me she loves me, and here she is telling Joe, who she has only known for an hour, she loves him. I've never seen Tammy act this way, but I haven't seen her around other people either. Does she tell every man she loves him?

This is crazy! I'll have to bring it up to Tammy after we leave the shop. I sat there for two and a half hours getting poked by a needle until my tree was perfect. Joe was grinning from ear to ear because he thought Tammy loved him, and she was going to break up with me and run into his arms! This was awkward because we'll see Joe again during our time here. Now Joe will be on the hunt for us all weekend.

Joe was a little bald guy, standing about 5'5" and of Mexican decent. Maybe Tammy saw something I didn't see in Joe, or maybe it was Joe's bald head that Tammy liked since Billy was sporting the bald look.

We paid for our tattoos and began our ride back to my sister's place to sleep over at her house before heading to the camp grounds the next day. I was trying to figure out the best way to confront Tammy about her actions with Joe.

After everyone had gone to bed, Tammy and I were getting ready to lie down for the night. I thought about it long and hard, and I asked Tammy, "What the hell are you doing telling Joe you love him for? do you love Joe? Because if you do, you can go sleep at Joe's house."

Tammy said, "What are you talking about? I never said I love Joe! I said I love Joe's work."

"Tammy, you said three or four times 'I love you,' so Joe thinks you love him. You cannot tell men you love them unless they are your relatives. You embarrassed me in front of my best friend and my brother by telling Joe you love him. You didn't say 'I love your work, Joe,' you said, 'I just love you.'"

Tammy got all upset over what I said she said, even though she meant it different and it just came out wrong. She was crying. She said this is what Billy does to her, always yelling at her, blaming her for everything.

I said, "I can't blame Billy for getting upset with you if you are telling other men you love them when you are with him. Now Joe thinks you really love him, and he will be looking for us tomorrow. Joe will flirt with you. I'm going to do nothing but watch because you gave him the wrong impression tonight."

Tammy laid there and cried like she was being picked on.

I said, "Tammy, if you want to go home, I'll take you to the airport in the morning. You can fly home if you want to."

Tammy said, "No, I want to be with you, but I don't want to fight."

"Well then, when we see Joe, you are going to have to fix it with him. Tammy, you should know by now I'm not a jealous man. I will not fight over a woman, ever. If you want someone else, just let me know. I'll step aside, then good luck to you. We've been dating for only a month. We haven't argued or even come close to fighting. I really like being with you Tammy, and I think we make a great couple. So please watch what you are saying to other men,;don't give them the impression you are interested in them by using the love word."

Tammy said, "I bet we won't see Joe tomorrow, or the rest of our trip here."

Everyone woke up around 8 am. We all decided to stop in town for breakfast before heading out to the rally. While we stood in line at Tom Thumb waiting for the food we ordered, guess who walked in, right in front of Tammy and I? Her friend Joe. He walked right up to Tammy.

"Hello, Tammy," he said with love in his eyes.

I bet Joe didn't sleep a wink last night thinking about how much Tammy loved him and had already made plans with her.

"Hi Joe," she said. She turned quickly toward me, feeling awkward and embarrassed.

I just shrugged my shoulders at Tammy with a smile on my face.

"I told you so," I said with a laugh.

"You were right," she said. "I'm so sorry for saying it. How'd you know Joe would act like this?"

"Tammy, if a good-looking woman keeps telling me she loves me, then I'm going to think she really does and pursue her."

I got to see how Tammy acts around other people and after our talk last night. I was worried about her being around thousands of others at the rally. Because the next time Tammy does it, she better damn well mean it and hope that man can give her a ride back to Oklahoma.

The Freedom Rally! Tents as far as the eye can see, rolling hills of green grass to set up your campsite for the weekend, pathways for bikers to ride in with their camping supplies behind their bikes. A stage high up on the hill for the different bands to play music throughout the night. I could smell the food already from the food vendors and grills from the camp-sites. The aroma was almost like being at the fair. Everyone there was happy to get away from life for a while, letting it all hang out. People were waving hello as we rode in to set up camp. No bedtime or wake up alarm for three days. Under God's good graces the sun will shine, and the stars will glow in the night sky.

After setting up our tents, we wandered up to the vendors to grab a bite to eat and look at what they had for souvenirs or something to purchase that I couldn't live without this year. Then Tammy and I strolled down to watch some of the rodeo events and drunk girls riding the mechanical bull, not doing very well either. The bands were getting fired up as we headed back down to the campsite later that afternoon. My brother and Shawn were sitting in their lawn chairs with drinks in hand watching people as they rode by. It was getting close to 5 pm. This is about the time some people have had too much to drink, and they start doing stupid things like riding their bike naked through the park. We all sat and watched for hours, laughing, drinking, and listening to the bands while grilling out some burgers for dinner.

Tammy was still acting weird about what took place the night before in the bedroom at my sister's house. This was wearing thin on me. She just wouldn't let it go. I was getting pissed. I told Tammy to drop it now, or I'd take her back to my sister's house, and she could find her own way back to Oklahoma.

"I came up here to have a good time," I said. "Once a year I come home to visit my family and go to the rally. Please don't ruin it for me."

The band stopped playing around 10:00 pm. It was quiet throughout the park. The lights dimmed on the stage. Then a guitarist started playing a solo which echoed through the night sky as everyone stood silently, listening to the sounds of the guitar through the giant speakers. It was the most beautiful solo I have ever heard someone play.

People walked up from their campsites to get a closer look at who the man was playing such a beautiful solo on his electric guitar. Everyone seemed to be in some kind of trance. As I listened to the notes being played, I looked around. I could see almost every couple holding each other and getting cozy, sitting in the grassy field close to the stage.

Tammy then moved between my legs she leaned back against me. I held her tightly while sitting in the grass under the stars. The guitarist put so much love into each cord. Everyone felt the love that night. For this 20-minute solo, I'm sure I wasn't the only person, the music brought back memories of the past, people whom I missed and loved very much who were absent from my life. I felt the solo was being played for Tammy and me. I was looking for something which would bring us closer together after such a bad start. It did just that. After he finished his solo, we all stood up with a long ovation.

The last band to hit the stage was up. They played from midnight until 2 am. Tammy wanted to get up closer to the stage. She pulled me through the crowd to get right up to the stage. The music was so loud it was ringing my ears. Tammy liked loud screaming music; I didn't. But I was with her and had to make sacrifices in this relationship.

I asked Tammy after a couple of songs if we could move back a little because the music was too loud for me. Tammy insisted on staying up front, leaning against the fence which separated the crowd from the band. Tammy looked over to her left she saw some girls standing in wife beater t-shirts. They were getting all the attention from some of the security, chatting with them and receiving beads.

The next thing I know Tammy threw off her sweatshirt onto my head and started acting like she was twenty years old again, trying to compete with those younger girls.

I was embarrassed at her actions. Quite a few girls asked me to tell Tammy to put her shirt back on. "You need to control her," they said. I asked Tammy a couple of times to put her shirt on, but with no avail. She told me she was too hot.

In Iowa when the sun goes down even in July it gets into the low fifties. It took me a while to lure Tammy away from the crowd. I could see the other girls were getting mad at the way Tammy was trying to get attention.

Finally, walking back to the tent, I was ready for some good loving, I could tell things were a lot better in our relationship. We had our arms around each other holding on tightly as we walked. The guitar solo brought us closer and letting Tammy act like a child for an hour was just what she needed. She was able to forget everything on her mind, shaking her boobs like she was young again. Believe me, Tammy was sexy for her age.

That night in the tent was unforgettable. We made love like never before. With the top off our tent, the moonbeam lit our little bedroom enough so our eyes could talk to each other while making love. Her skin was so soft, like a freshly bathed baby. I touched her tenderly unlike I have any other woman. I wanted Tammy. I wanted to keep Tammy. We could hardly keep from letting the world hear the passion which filled our souls that night. This was not just a night of heated passion; it was love for one another which filled our hearts deeply.

The next morning around 10 am we decided to ride into Algona to have some breakfast at the Catholic Church. During the rally the Church serves breakfast to the rally goers for five dollars a plate, making money for the church. We were given three pancakes, scrambled eggs, sausage links, and coffee.

While eating breakfast, I told the others Tammy and I were going to ride back into Fort Dodge to spend the day. I wanted to show Tammy my old stomping grounds and visit some relatives. But we were going to visit the Grotto first since it was on the way back to Fort Dodge. We needed to see this while we were in Iowa, since Shawn and I were Catholics.

The Grotto is in Westbend, Iowa. It's the Eighth Wonder of the World. A Catholic Priest built it, traveling around the world collecting rocks to be used in its construction. It's the first time I had been there. We were truly amazed at the beauty and the story which was put into the project. It was a story of Jesus Christ Each path takes you to a new journey during his life, as written in the Bible.

We gathered around our bikes in the parking lot after touring the Grotto. "I'm not sure if we will be back tonight," I said. "If not, we'll be back in the morning to help take tents down and pack up our supplies for our trip back home."

My brother and my best friend, Shawn, said they were going to ride some country roads to see the sites around Iowa. They'd return to the rally later in the day to check on our things.

Tammy and I started back to Fort Dodge on my bike. After what took place in the tent last night, we were in love, inseparable. Nothing could tear us apart from this day forward. We laughed, kissed, acting like young lovers should, always complimenting each other; by just being together.

CHAPTER 16

Home Town Fort Dodge

When we arrived back to Fort Dodge, Tammy said she was a little chilly on the bike ride back. She asked if there was a store where she could find a sweat suit until it warmed up outside.

I took Tammy to Deckers, a sporting goods store in Fort Dodge, where she found the perfect light green sweat suit for her to wear.

I pulled the tags off the suit and went up front to pay for it while Tammy went into the dressing room to change. When Tammy came out of the dressing room, I said, "You look perfect." I just stood there with my eyes looking at her, not even blinking. Tammy was so beautiful, and I loved her so much. Tammy was blushing as she grabbed my arm and pulled me out of the store. I was so happy, and I wanted her to know it.

Fort Dodge was a small mid-western town of about 50,000 people. Nothing has really changed much since I moved away back in 1977 looking for bigger dreams. There weren't many places to work unless you were in retail or the restaurant business. Most of the money came from the farmers in the area, which kept the city alive during the economy crunch. Most of the homes within the city were run down, along with the streets, which were full of potholes. Riding through the city, looking at all the empty buildings that were once open booming with businesses when I was a child, was depressing.

Tammy and I went to my Uncle Bill's house. I hadn't seen Bill since my mother's funeral in March of 2006. Tammy and I sat in the kitchen having coffee with Bill and his wife. We shared our story of how we met online. About thirty minutes into our visit, Tammy was talking with my Uncle Bill. Tammy said, "I'm going to Marry Jim!" That caught me by surprise; we had never brought marriage up before. I would have been happy with, "I love you, Jim." But I was ok with her words because I was in love with Tammy since the first time I laid eyes on her at the nursery.

I wanted to take Tammy to a place where we could just be together not being bothered by anyone, so I took her to Armstrong Park. The park had a creek running through the back. I wanted to show Tammy where as a boy I'd seine for minnows and chubs and net a few crawfish for fishing bait— after pulling the leeches off of my legs when I came out of the water.

Of course, that was back in the 70's when the creeks ran waist high and weren't so polluted with trash. The water now was about eight inches deep; in some places twelve inches. You could still see the minnows swimming in certain places under the rocks. Tammy pulled up her pant legs to walk in the water looking for some rocks to take back home for her flower beds.

Tammy found a few rocks she just had to have. She would throw them up on the bank for me to pile them up. Then she started splashing me with big rocks, laughing. So like the gentleman I was, I took off my boots and chased her down, splashing her with both hands in the water. We spent three hours playing like young kids in the water. Tammy jumped on my back, and I carried her to the sandy creek bed. She was reaching around kissing me on my face, laughing with joy. We walked up and down that creek bed holding hands with an occasional kiss to show our love for one another.

After we left the park, we headed into town to grab a bite to eat before going back to my sister's house to spend some time with her. We stopped at The Brickyard, a little bar and restaurant. I would stop here to have dinner and a drink before going back to Oklahoma every weekend when I came to town to visit my mother before she passed away from breast cancer. I did this for the last three months of my mother's life.

Tammy and I ordered club sandwiches, fries, and sodas. While we waited for our food, I grabbed Tammy's hand. I thanked her for being here with me. I knew we were in love, but neither of us has used the LOVE word yet.

I told Tammy I never wanted to be away from her. "When we get back to Oklahoma, I hope we get to finish what we've started. I've waited a long time for someone like you, Tammy. You are so beautiful. I hope you feel the same way about me."

"Yes, I do feel the same," she said, as she looked into my eyes. "I'm sorry for the other night with Joe; I promise to make it up to you. I thought you were going to be like Billy at first, yelling at me about other guys, or for every little mistake I make. I was the one who was wrong, and for that I'm sorry. I'd like to finish what we started, and I meant what I said to your Uncle Bill today."

What could I say? I kissed her.

Our food came out, and I looked at our club's; it was ham, mayo, and bread. I looked at the waitress, and I said "we ordered a club sandwich! "

The waitress said, "That is a club sandwich," looking at me like I was goofy.

I asked the waitress, "Where's the turkey, tomato, lettuce, and bacon?"

The waitress said, "We don't have those things."

I asked, "Then why do you offer a club sandwich? Why don't you just call it a ham sandwich? How is this called a club? In Oklahoma, a club sandwich has ham, turkey, bacon, lettuce, tomato, in between three slices of Toasted bread, with toothpicks holding it together."

The waitress said, "That is our club sandwich," then she walked back into the kitchen.

I wasn't mad or trying to cause a scene; I was just wondering if they forgot the rest of the sandwich. Maybe as it was passed down the sandwich line, someone forgot to add their part of the club.

I told Tammy, "If I had ordered the T-bone steak, I would have gotten the T-bone, 'cause that's how they do it in Iowa." We laughed and enjoyed our lunch together.

We rode back to my sister's house in, Callender, Iowa, just seven miles west of Fort Dodge. It's a quiet little town of around three hundred people. The town sat in the middle of nowhere. Corn fields lay on all four corners of the town. Callender had one four-way stop in the middle of town, leading out of town either way you turned. A library and a bank sat on the main street, along with my sister's house.

My sister and Tammy got along quite well. I was able to sit and visit with Gary, my sister's husband, in the living room while he and I watched some television while sitting on the couch. After all the traveling we've done the past couple days, Tammy and I decided to turn in early. We went to bed around 10:00 pm.

After spending the night at my sister's house, we got up early and had breakfast with my sister before riding back to the rally to help pack up our tent and supplies.

We had one day left before heading back to Oklahoma. My sister wanted to have a cookout for us. Besides, we needed to thank her for getting the campsites paid for in advance for us. We all pitched in to help them buy the food for the cookout.

CHAPTER 17

My Sister's House

We all helped grill up ribs and brats with potato salad and beans. Of course, drinking and storytelling went on as well. My sister was telling Tammy all my childhood secrets. This went on for hours into the night. We built a fire, sat in lawn chairs in a circle and shared stories from the past and present. Another perfect night under the stars. The nights in Iowa seem so much darker, and the stars glowed so brightly. It's like there are just millions of stars shining. and you can see them all. Nothing like in Oklahoma where there doesn't seem to be as many. They aren't as bright there either. Maybe that's why they call Iowa God's country; you're closer to heaven, where the stars shine brighter.

It's getting close to saying goodbye to my sister for another year. I've been saying goodbye to her every year for about fifteen years now. Every year it is the same thing; I tear up as I'm hugging her goodbye. I was going to have to do that again in the morning, this time in front of my new girl-friend, which didn't bother me, that's family closeness and love. This is something Tammy's kids could use in their life. I've seen it up close while being with her kids. They hate first until you kiss their butt. Then it's up to them if you're accepted into their circle.

As we sat around the fire, I could see everyone's face from the glow of the flame. I thought to myself how lucky I am to have such good friends and a wonderful family with me sharing these moments in life, moments we will never get back once they are gone.

Like I said, saying goodbye is not my strong point, I dilly-dallied around until everyone else said their thank you's and goodbyes to my sister and Gary. It was my turn once again. I started to tear up as I hugged my sister. I could hardly tell my sister I loved her with the giant frog in my throat, but hey that's how family does it.

I climbed into the back seat of my truck with Tammy. I let my best friend Shawn drive us home. Tammy and I held hands all the way back to Oklahoma, and I hated the trip back seemed so short. I wanted to spend more time with Tammy. I was showing her how family loves and the good person I was. But even good times must come to an end.

CHAPTER 18

Billy's Back

Shawn pulled my truck into the driveway about 5 pm. Everyone was dead tired after the 8-hour drive back. Tammy grabbed her things, and she left in her car after kissing me goodbye. My best friend Shawn asked if he could leave his bike and pick it up the next day after work. My brother went on home to do the same thing the rest of us had in mind, get some more sleep.

There was no doubt Tammy and I came a long way in our relationship those three days in Iowa. We were in love, but who was going to be first to say it? I walked out back to my patio and sat down while I had a smoke. I played back every moment Tammy and I made love, kissed or just laughed out loud together on our trip to Iowa. She was on my mind every minute of the day since the first time I met her.

Around 7 pm Tammy called me; she was mad.

Tammy asked me, "Do you know what Billy did while we were in Iowa?"

Crap! Billy is back again, I thought to myself.

I asked Tammy, "What did Billy do this time?"

Tammy said, "Billy sprayed a weed killer on my thirty-year-old hosta's. Then he went out in the garden and pulled up all the tomato plants. Billy threw them on the ground. He did the same thing with the pepper plants. I'm pissed Billy did that. He even broke some of the planting pots I had on the table."

I said "Tammy the tomato plants and pepper plants were Billy's could he do whatever he wants to do with them, right? Billy had no right to spray your hosta's. Call Billy and ask why he did this."

"I'm not going to call Billy asking him why he did it," she said. "Billy will say he didn't, and then he'll come over to my house. I don't want Billy here anymore. You're my boyfriend now. My friend Lucy gave me those hostas. We planted them together. Now they are all brown and sick looking because of what Billy did."

"I'm sorry, Tammy. I'll come by after work tomorrow and help you to see if we can save them. Why would Billy do that anyway? Why is He acting like a child?"

Tammy said, "Because Billy is an ass, he does things like this to hurt me so maybe I'll go running back to him."

"I don't think hurting you will bring you running back to his arms," I said. "I'm sorry, Tammy there's nothing we can do about it right now. It's getting dark out, but I'll come by tomorrow after work."

After we hung up I couldn't think of why Billy would do something so childish. Billy's a 46-year-old man. If I knew Tammy, she would probably call Billy tonight, ripping him another one. But she's afraid him. I have no idea why. It's been a month since Billy had made his presence known. I guessed Billy was burning off some left-over anger. Maybe he came over to talk to Tammy while we were gone and it pissed him off.

Will he leave her alone now? This was the second time Tammy had been gone with me for a couple of days. You'd think Billy would get the hint by now unless Billy thinks he's given her enough time to miss him and wonders if Tammy is ready to take him back.

CHAPTER 19

The Bathing Suit

By the middle of July, things were going very well for Tammy and me. She hadn't heard from Billy since we got back from Iowa, although he had called hanging up the phone a few times when she answered it. She said Billy calls from a blocked number, so she knows it was him.

I had been spending more time over at Tammy's house helping her fix a few things which needed fixing. I'd go over to her house every night after work. Tammy would be running around her yard in this God-awful bikini. It was old with a floral pattern, dirty from years of wearing it every day. She had this on every day when I came to her house. As her boyfriend, I wanted to tell Tammy that it was one ugly bathing suit, but I spared her feelings. I tried not to look at it.

Tammy would be running from the front yard to the backyard watering her plants or weeding out her flower beds in that nasty bikini. I can't imagine what the neighbors thought seeing Tammy in the same ugly bikini every day with sweat rolling off her body like a hot sweaty carpenter while holding her 32oz jug of wine. Tammy was like a one-armed gardener, with her jug of wine held in one hand at all times.

I'd ask Tammy to stop running around so much and take a break with me in the shade. I worked in the hot sun all day installing a privacy fence. I needed some shade time. Tammy would stop for a bit, then go back to roaming her yard. She was hyper all the time like she was on speed or something.

I wanted to hear more new information about Billy Wolf. It seemed like every time I asked Tammy for more information about Billy she'd start talking about her ex-husband, Edward, and how that bitch took her family away from her. For some reason, she was avoiding telling me anything new about Billy.

"Stop saying that, Tammy. Your husband chooses someone different, So what! Let it go, move on with your life. Would it bother you if all I talked about was my ex-wife every time we were together? How can we have a healthy a relationship, if you refuse to let Edward go?"

Tammy said, "That bitch led Edward on! That's why I hate the bitch."

"Why do you say such mean things about this woman? Why is everyone else to blame, except you? Are you perfect? Was your marriage perfect? I think you started sleeping with Billy to get back at Edward. Am I right about that?"

"No, I didn't start seeing Billy to get back at Edward," she said. "I called Billy to help me get through my divorce. I asked Billy to tell Edward to pack his things and leave. Billy did that for me."

"Tammy, were you still married to Edward when you started your relationship with Billy?" I asked.

"Yes, I was," she said. "Why do you ask?"

"I think you did it to get back at Edward, thinking he'd come back running to you. Did Billy lead you on like that girl led Edward on? Tammy, you're not perfect. What you did was out of anger to get back at Edward. But it backfired on you. Billy is a pain in your ass, and he won't go away now.

"This is because of your doings, Tammy. You have to take control of Billy's actions and put a stop to it. I won't let you use me to make Billy jealous. If you're looking for attention from two guys fighting over you, you need to get another player in this game."

Every day for the next week all Tammy talked about was Billy and Edward, how they did everything together. In high school, they would party together, and after high school, they even worked at the same job together for years. Billy even taught Edward how to hunt. Billy was good with guns. He's a great hunter. "Billy has taken me to his parent's house to shoot guns before," she said.

This went on every night. I was getting tired of hearing about these two men in her life. Plus, Tammy running around in her dirty bikini doing yard work. It was just about all I could stand.

Finally, I asked Tammy to stop talking about them so much. "I'm here now, Tammy." She'd stop for about five or ten minutes, and then something would bring her back to those two again.

"I understand those two men have been part of your life for most of your adulthood," I said. "I feel like I'm being compared or I have to live up to their standards. Breaking your things to show my love for you, is that what you want? This is not fair to me, so please let them go, or let me go.

"I understand Edward is your ex-husband, and you have children together. You should finish raising your children with

Edward. You'll need to talk often with him. But you have no ties to Billy. He was your boyfriend who was mean to you and treated you like dirt. You owe Billy nothing. I prefer from now on not to hear any more stories about Billy unless you have information about him I need to know."

"I'm sorry about going off on a tangent, talking about Billy and Edward all the time," she said. "I'll watch what I'm saying from now on."

I wanted to know more about Billy. I wanted to ask Tammy more questions about him. Tammy wasn't going to offer anything. I needed to ask the right questions to get the right answers from her.

"Tammy, am I safe being here with you all the time?" I asked. "Do you think Billy would confront me, or sneak up behind me? You have mentioned Billy would follow you and the other guys around you've dated. Do you think Billy has followed us?"

"Yes, Jim, I bet Billy has followed us. One time Billy followed me and this guy to Walmart. Billy would stand down at the end of an isle watching us. Each isle he'd be standing there. I told the guy I was with Billy was here watching us. After a while, he got spooked and broke it off. Billy wasn't going to do anything to us. Billy would just scare guys off, following us around. He's not a tuff guy at all, and he just looks mean when he shaves his head."

"So then you and Billy would get back together after he ran off the guy you were dating. Because his plan worked all the time. Is that your plan for me, Tammy?"

"I'd call Billy, asking what he was doing following me. Then we would get back together after he came over to talk. Then I'd have to tell Billy everything I did with the other guy."

"Tell Billy what?" I asked. "Where you went? What you did?"

"No, I had to tell him if we had sex," she said. "How we did it, if I liked it, in detail, because Billy had to know. He was just weird in that way, I guess."

"Oh my God, Billy is one sick dude. Devonna was right about him being a deviant. I don't understand how you can think this is ok? How could you be with someone who is like that? Why would you tell him about your sex with someone else? Tammy, you really need to get away from him."

"That's why I contacted you, Jim," she said. "I saw you were a good person. I need someone good in my life. I'm tired of fighting with Billy all the time. He scares me, and I know Billy is on drugs and lies to me all the time about other women.

So now Billy has probably followed us, or me, back to my house at one time or another. I'm still not sure if Billy was a violent man or just a stalker. I haven't heard any stories from Tammy about anything he has done violent, just stalking people. I made sure when I rode my Harley to her house when leaving I'd watch the road, all oncoming traffic. I didn't want Billy running me off the road while riding my bike. I don't know what to think at this point. Billy hadn't come around or made his presence known lately. Maybe he'd moved on. Who knows?

CHAPTER 20

Meeting Lucy

I took Tammy out Saturday night. We hadn't been anywhere since coming back from Iowa. After I started going over to Tammy's house, she just wanted to stay home all the time. We needed a break. I was tired of listening to her talking about Billy and Edward all the time.

Tammy invited her friend Lucy and her husband to meet us at the club. Tammy said, "Jim, I want you to meet my best friend Lucy tonight. Lucy and I grew up together around Braden Park. We've known each other since we were six years old. Billy doesn't like my friends, so I don't get to see them very often, only when Billy goes hunting for the weekend. So, I invited Lucy and her husband to meet us tonight."

When Lucy and her husband arrived at the club, my first impression of Lucy was she was stuck somewhere in the seventies. Her clothes were from that era. I pictured Lucy sitting all day in her home wearing a moo-moo with a lot of cats. She had long dark frizzy hair with split ends, not professionally done by someone with a license in quite some time. Lucy was the kind of friend every girl had, because they weren't too cute, so you didn't have to worry about your boyfriend hitting on her. She was the type of friend who only wanted to hear the gossip, but never offered any help. She was only good at giving Tammy advice on how to handle Billy.

Tammy introduced Lucy and her husband to me. "Lucy, this is Jim, my boyfriend." After saying our hellos, Tammy and Lucy sat together at the end of the table. Tammy started telling Lucy everything Billy has done to us since dating me. After Tammy filled Lucy in on things, they took off to the dance floor. They'd only come back for a sip of their drink from time to time. This went on for a couple of hours. Was I supposed to sit with Lucy's husband, keeping him company while watching the girls dance? Tammy came over to the table telling me some younger guys wanted her number. Tammy was all smiles with the attention she was receiving from a group of twenty-year-old boys flirting with her.

I asked Tammy to walk over to the bar with me so I could talk to her alone since I haven't been able to talk with her since her friend Lucy arrived.

I said, "Tammy, I brought you here so we could spend some time alone. I wanted to dance with you and spend some quality time just being together building our relationship. When you told me your friend was coming, I didn't plan on babysitting your friend's husband all night while you danced with Lucy. I would have canceled our date if I had known this. You and I needed the break away from your house and every-thing else going on there. But you've been with your friend Lucy every minute since they've shown up. If you plan to spend the rest of the night on the dance floor with your friend and flirting with those younger boys over there, then I'll just go to my house tonight."

Tammy flew off the handle. She started making a scene. She was pouting like a child raising her voice at me. People were looking at me, as I stood there listening to her tantrum.

I looked at Tammy. I was embarrassed by her actions. I said, "our date is over now. I'm going home. I don't have time for this, Tammy."

I walked out the door. Standing outside in the parking lot, I remembered we drove Tammy's car. I had a 5-mile walk back to my house. As I was walking on the side of the road back to my house, Tammy sped on past me, letting me continue my walk home. I wasn't going to call or text her the next day because she was acting like a child. Once again, Tammy was seeking attention from a table of younger guys, just like she did with Joe in Iowa. Why did Tammy need to be the center of attention all the time? Maybe she didn't really like me. Maybe she was embarrassed to be out with me in public. I wasn't going to let her treat me like that; I deserved better.

The next morning, I asked my brother take me over to Tammy's house to pick up my Jeep. I jumped into my Jeep and I went home. If Tammy wanted to talk to me, she could call me.

Three days later, I received a text from Tammy saying she was sorry for her actions Saturday night and she missed me.

I immediately sent a text back to Tammy because I'd been on pins and needles waiting to hear from her again. I'd almost given up. I figured she went back to Billy like she always did after her breakups. Tammy always had Billy to fall back on when her relationships failed.

Tammy sent me a text asking if I would come over to her house tonight after work because she had missed me she wanted to see me again.

Of course I was going over to see her. I missed Tammy too! It was breaking my heart I hadn't heard from her in a couple of days. I missed her smile, her hugs, and kisses. I couldn't wait to grab hold of her again, looking into her eyes and telling her how much I missed her.

I pulled into Tammy's driveway around 5 pm, right after work without stopping at my house. I couldn't wait to get my, "I missed you" kiss.

Tammy and I sat in lawn chairs under the tree out front of her home in a shaded grassy area which was perfect for a making up talk.

I told Tammy, "What you did Saturday night to me was wrong. You embarrassed me in front of your friends and everyone else there."

Tammy said, "I'm sorry, Jim, for the way I acted. Why did you leave?"

I said, "Because you were cussing at me, Tammy. If I let you treat me like that once, then every time you get angry with me you'll do it again. So I put a stop to it. I will not be treated like that by anyone, including you. Why is it you need to have attention from other men all the time? I hope I've shown you I'm not jealous. I was going to go home letting you have your time with Lucy and the table of younger boys. I took us out to have fun Tammy, not to entertain your friends. I wanted to be alone with you, slow dancing all night."

Tammy said, "I never get to see Lucy anymore because Billy doesn't like my friends. That's why my friends don't come around. I guess I got carried away when I saw Lucy. I forgot about you. Those younger boys kept asking me for my number while Lucy and I were dancing."

I said, "Tammy, maybe you should have told them you were with me and left the dance floor. But you left me at the table with Lucy's husband while you just kept on letting those younger boys flirt with you, taking it all in. Tammy, you pulled the same thing in Iowa, with Joe. If this is how you are going to be when we go out, then I'll step aside and find someone who wants to be with me."

I said, "Tammy, I thought I was your boyfriend."

Tammy said, "You are my boyfriend, Jim."

I asked Tammy, "Why does it matter if Billy doesn't like your friends? If I'm your new boyfriend, your friends are welcome to come over anytime they want."

Tammy said, "I'm sorry, Jim. Sometimes I don't realize my actions could be hurting someone. I'm with you because I like you a lot. You are a good man, not always yelling at me like Billy does all the time."

Tammy said, "Let's go out back and get the fire pit going."

The talk was over; we had things settled between us. I was the boyfriend still, and it was time to just enjoy each other's company until well after dark. I watched Tammy poking at the fire she had going. She was so beautiful in the glow of the flame. Tammy sipped on her wine as we enjoyed being together after our three-day separation.

CHAPTER 21

The Master Bedroom

We went inside Tammy's house after the fire burnt out. I sat in her bedroom watching television while she showered from all the sweating she did in the yard before I got there.

After Tammy showered, I told her the smell of the carpet in her bedroom was just horrible. It needed to be removed. I told Tammy I would help her remove the nasty, stained carpet and install a new wood flooring in her bedroom if she bought the flooring.

Tammy asked, "I would love that, Jim. When can we do it? I'm ready to start fixing up my house and start a new life with you. Your house is so beautiful; I want you to help me make mine beautiful too."

The following Friday after work, I headed to Tammy's house to help her remove the old stained carpet. We would run to Lowe's to get the flooring as soon as the carpet was removed from her bedroom floor. I told Tammy it would take all weekend to lay the flooring and trim in her bedroom.

I told Tammy, "Don't make any plans to do anything else," because I wouldn't do it alone.

It took five big trash bags to clean what Tammy had under her bed. I found pills, dirty magazines, and things without a name. I have never seen someone's room so nasty. The smell was just horrible. We rolled up the carpet to carry it out to the garage. Dirt just poured out from the fibers all over me. Tammy just laughed the whole time.

Saturday morning Tammy and I starting putting her new floor down. I had the trim out in the garage on saw horses. I asked Tammy to paint the trim so it would be dry when we needed it tomorrow. That night about 10:30 pm Lori came into Tammy's room.

Lori asked, "Mom will you take me to a friend's house?"

Tammy said, "Lori it's too late, I'm not getting out this time of night."

They argued back and forth for a few minutes. Then Lori blurted out to Tammy, "I hope Billy shoots you!" Then she stomped out of Tammy's room back up to her room, slamming the door.

I couldn't believe what I had just heard out of Lori's mouth, and neither could Tammy. We just stood there in silence looking at each other. What the hell was that about, Billy shooting Tammy? Would Billy do that? This brings a new light on things. Maybe Billy would use a gun on someone.

Sunday night around 9:00 pm we finished the flooring and trim. I put Tammy's bed back together so she could sleep in it before work Monday morning. I had driven my Jeep over to her house that day. I could pick up my tools on my way to the job site in the morning.

Tammy asked, "Will you spend the night with me since it is late? I will wake you up at 6 am when I get up. You can drive home get your truck and trailer, then swing by here get your tools. What do you think about that?"

Well, Tammy did have her arms around me, kissing me, saying please over and over. How could I say no to that?

"Ok, I will stay, but wake me up when you get up."

It was my first time spending the night with Tammy at her house. I probably won't sleep real sound being in a strange bed for the first time. I really wasn't comfortable with staying, but I did. I slept lightly all night. Billy was in the back of my mind because of what Lori said to Tammy about Billy shooting her. I made my decision to stay, but I kept thinking to myself I needed to put a deadbolt on the garage door leading out to the side yard of the house. A tall wooden fence and bushes covered it.

CHAPTER 22

The Jeep

Monday morning at 6 am, just like Tammy promised, she was getting into the shower I was getting my clothes on so I could head back to my house to pick up my truck and trailer. I noticed the cable was out on Tammy's television. It was all white snow screen. She keeps her television on all night, but cable goes out all the time. I yelled into her bathroom, "Goodbye, see you after work tonight."

I walked out to my jeep feeling good, ready to start my day. I put the key in and, turned the ignition on, but nothing happened. It was dead. "Did I leave my lights on?" I asked myself. I checked everything. Nothing was left on. I guess my battery was dead.

I walked back up Tammy's house and knocked on the door. Tammy opened the door in her housecoat.

Tammy asked, "Did you forget something? "

"Do you have some jumper cables," I asked. "My battery is dead."

I was embarrassed to ask her, but I needed a jump so I could get to my job before 8:00 am like I promised my customer.

Tammy said, "I have some in my car, let me get dressed first."

As I turned to walk back to my Jeep, I saw some wires hanging underneath. I thought that was odd so I walked over to look. Not once did I think Billy has been here during the night. I opened the hood, and I found all my wiring cut from the harness going into the fuse box. I through my hands in the air said, "Damn you, Billy!" shaking my head with frustration as I looked at the damage Billy did to my Jeep during the night while I was sleeping.

"What's wrong?" she asked. "Jim, is everything ok?"

I said, "Billy cut all my wiring, Tammy, that's what's wrong with my Jeep."

I was pissed Billy would stoop to that level to cut a man's wiring in the middle of the night. I wanted to know who this Billy was and what is he up to.

"Tammy, call the police so I can make out a report have Billy arrested," I said. "I'm not going to put up with this senseless crap. Billy isn't man enough to meet me face to face. Instead, he sneaks over in the middle of the night, messing with my things."

I was almost mad enough to leave Tammy for good.

I looked inside the Jeep, finding my glove box wide open. "Billy took my insurance card with my address on it, and the remote to my garage door," I said. "Now I must change the code on my garage door opener because Billy has the address to my house."

"I'm sorry, Jim," she said, "He won't do anything else. Billy was just mad at me, that's all. Please don't leave me. Billy won't bother us anymore. I promise Jim, Billy's nothing but a coward."

Tammy kept on apologizing for Billy's actions. She could see I wasn't happy with what Billy had done to my Jeep during the night.

A policeman pulled up shortly after Tammy called them so I could make out the report and show him what Billy did to my Jeep. The officer knew Billy Wolf. He was one of the policemen here last year when Billy brought a gun to Tammy's house, telling her he was going to kill himself.

The officer his took a report, saying there was nothing they could do since we didn't catch Billy in the act. "But I know Billy Wolf well," the officer mentioned in passing. "Billy has been in a lot of trouble with the law."

The officer told me he would patrol the area throughout the day. He had asked Tammy what Billy was driving so he could keep an eye out for his truck while patrolling the neighborhood. Tammy told the officer Billy drove a teal green Chevy truck.

"I noticed the cable was out this morning," I said. "Maybe you should check your cable lines since Billy has been here."

Tammy and the officer saw that Billy cut her cable line, phone line, and air-conditioning line. Tammy couldn't find her cat, Jack, anywhere, either. Jack was an old yellow calico cat that just hung around the garage. Tammy would leave the garage door open about six inches for Jack to come in at night to sleep in the garage. The second cat I have liked my whole life, and he was gone.

I noticed brake fluid around the rear tire of Tammy's car. I walked over to look, and I saw Billy had also cut her rear brake line!

"We have something else to fix, Tammy," I said. "Billy cut your rear brake line too."

I was thinking to myself, while I was sleeping inside Tammy's house, Billy was outside stalking us. This guy is giving me the creeps, sneaking around in the middle of the night. I'll not stay at Tammy's house again until I put a dead-bolt on the garage door leading out to the side yard. There's just something about that door which keeps coming into play in my head. I have no idea what Billy might do, but I'm not going to take any chances even though what Billy has done has been harmless up till now. They'd been pranks that anyone acting like a child would do.

I returned to Tammy's house after work, about 3:00 pm to splice all my wiring back together. Tammy had her cable and phone line fixed. The air-conditioning was going to cost her $500.00 to fix. She didn't have the money because she loaned Billy $10,000.00, so her credit cards were maxed out. Being that it was the middle of July and not October, I said I'd pay for it.

"I'll give you the $500.00 to fix your air-conditioning," I said.

The policeman who was there earlier that morning stopped by as I was working on my Jeep. The officer asked, "How's it coming along, Jim?"

"I'm getting it, almost done," I said. "The wire is color coded, which makes it easier."

He could see I was hot and sweaty, working in the hot July sun. The officer told me not to worry about guys like

Billy. They think they are good, but they always get caught in the end.

If Tammy wasn't so special to me, I would have left her after fixing my Jeep. Maybe she was right, and Billy wouldn't do anything else. But Tammy said that all the time and Billy does it again. Was he just doing one last thing, to get her good for breaking up with him? What's the story between Tammy and Billy? Maybe Billy was teaching me, the new boyfriend a lesson, trying to run me off. Since I have never done anything like this before, after a break up I couldn't come up with a reason why Billy would do this, other than just being, downright evil.

I never took my Jeep back to Tammy's house again. From that day on I drove my truck. This way I could lock it up and set the alarm. I wanted to see a picture of Billy in case he drove by or I spotted him around my house, since he now had my address.

Tammy said, "I'm sorry, Jim. I'll pay you back your money as soon as I can. First thing tomorrow I'm going to file a protective order on Billy to keep him away from me and my kids. He's gone too far this time, and I don't want to lose you, Jim."

CHAPTER 23

Protective Order

Tammy kept her word. She went right to the courthouse that morning.

"Billy was sitting in the courtroom," she said. "He was giving me the "wolf look" to try to scare me."

"What the hell is the wolf look?" I asked.

"It's the wolf look to scare people," she said. "I just gave it back to Billy. Then he'd start talking to me, saying things to try and scare me. I asked the judge to tell Billy to stop talking to me.

"The judge told Billy to stop talking to me. She told Billy she better not see him in her courtroom again."

The judge told Billy he was not to have any contact what so ever and not get within 500 yards of my children or me. Also, he'd had better stay away from my house.

"The judge gave me a 6-month protective order," she said. "The judge told the Bailiff to hold Billy in the hallway until I was gone from the parking lot."

"Billy was pissed when I told him I didn't want to see him anymore," she said. "I told Billy to stay away from me and my children as I left the courtroom. This will either make Billy go away or really make him mad now."

"I don't understand how a man on probation for a gun charge can have a protective order put on him for stalking and trespassing during the night," I said, "and nothing happens to him? Seem's like the law only works for the bad guys. I thought probation meant you couldn't get into any kind of trouble during your probationary period."

Tammy dug out a photo of Billy for me to see when she returned home. Billy stood 5'9" and 180 lbs. He was bald with a mustache, not really tough looking. Just a lanky build. Billy had beady eyes only a sneaky looking man would have. Someone who'd only do things behind someone's back or during the night time hours.

"I hate it when Billy shaves his head," she said. "He only does it to piss me off."

"Billy looks like a coward to me," I said. "Not one smile in any of the pictures you've shown me of Billy. A lot of men are like that, not smiling in pictures."

I needed to know more about Billy, who he was, what he's capable of doing. Now that Tammy had a protective order on Billy maybe he'd stop now. If Billy gets caught he goes to prison, no questions asked. I'm the man who will send him to prison for being stupid. Now all I had to do is figure out what night Billy would be coming over to do something stupid again and catch him in the act. One thing for sure, it would be during the night. But what night, would he be coming?

CHAPTER 24

Lunch date

Tammy invited me to have lunch with her where she works. Of course, she notified her work of the protective order she had on Billy. The guards were on alert to watch out for him being on the premises.

I walked to the door where Tammy told me to meet her. I was greeted by a security guard asking me who I was looking for.

The security guard reminded me of Barney Fife on the Andy Griffith show. He was a small man, standing only about 5' 5" weighing about 135 pounds in full uniform.

I said, "I'm here to see Tammy Simmons, we have a lunch date."

The security guard said, "Tammy was here. She went back inside to get something to eat. You are supposed to wait here with me until she returns."

Tammy came walking down the hall with something she picked up from the cafeteria. She was all smiles and happy to see me waiting for her.

Tammy asked me, "Have you met, Jim? He is our security guard. He protects me. Don't you, Jim?"

The security guard said, "Yes, I do watch out for you, Tammy."

Tammy looked at him with the innocent smile she uses to get out of trouble.

"Jim, this is my boyfriend, Jim. Isn't that funny, I have two Jim's protecting me," Tammy said with a giggle in her voice.

Once again Tammy was loving the attention, from the two of us.

The security guard said with a grin, "We have met. Now I don't want you two going too far out of my sight! You never know what Billy might do. We are keeping a good eye out for him. He better not come around here while I'm on watch."

We walk to find a place to be alone. "Tammy, what the hell was that all about?" I asked. "I thought he was going to hold me on gun point until you came back. Why are they on high alert over Billy?"

Tammy said, "I told them what Billy has been doing to me and that he might try to come up here to see me. So, they walk me to my car after work just in case Billy is in the parking lot waiting for me."

Tammy and I walked out into the grassy area up on a little hill looking over the Broken Arrow Expressway. We sat there enjoying our short time together under the sun, while she ate her lunch. It was another beautiful day, not a cloud in the sky. The birds were full of song as they flew from one tree to another. Tammy and I sat there during her lunch break, not talking about Billy at all.

Tammy said, "It's time for me to go back in; my lunch hour is over. Are you coming over tonight, Georgie Porgie?"

"Yes, I will come over right after work around six tonight," I said.

We walked back to the door Tammy came out of. Jim, the security guard, was mad, yelling at us. "I told you two not to wonder out of my sight! I was looking all over the grounds and searching the building for you. I was about to call the police before I saw you walking back."

I'm wondering to myself, why is he freaking out? It's not like Billy is a sniper or something. Tammy has a protective order, not a warrant out for his arrest. Why is he making such a big deal over this?

The security guard asked Tammy, "How can I protect you if you wonder off like you just did?"

Tammy said, "I'm sorry, Jim," with that look again, as she hugged him. "I won't do it again. We just went up the hill to enjoy the beautiful weather and the sunshine for lunch."

Tammy said as she turned toward me, "I'll see you tonight, Jim," then she walked back into the building with the cute little walk she had.

While walking out to my truck, I was wondering to myself why the security guard was so upset over us having a quiet lunch together alone on top of the grassy hill. Am I missing something here? What has Tammy told them about Billy? What do they know about Billy? Maybe it's how they handle things when someone has a protective order because of all the shootings which have happened at places of employment. But he seemed on high alert for some reason and eager to catch Billy.

CHAPTER 25

Security Cameras

Things were quiet until the following Saturday. I spent the night with Tammy again. It stormed all night, heavy rain and thunder. When I woke up to gray skies Sunday morning, I found Tammy's yard statues sitting on the hood of our vehicles. On Tammy's car was a cat statue and on my truck hood was a Penny statue. What a moron, I thought to myself. Billy was an uneducated sissy hiding in the darkness.

"I've had enough of Billy's crap," I said. "Tammy, I'm going to Lowe's to buy a security camera. I'll catch Billy's ass now! I'm getting a deadbolt for the garage door, too. This guy is creepy, hanging around here during the night like Jack the Ripper."

While I was at Lowe's, I bought the last security system they had. It was a black and white system. At this point, I didn't care. I wanted to catch Billy and have him on tape. The hard part was finding a television which had a VHS for recording tapes. The good news was my brother, who was a truck driver, happen to have one he used out on the road to watch movies when he stopped for the night.

My brother told me I could stop over at his house and pick it up. I could use it until I caught Billy. He said he'd have to look for the remote that went to the television.

While outside of Tammy's house, I looked for the perfect spot for my cameras. It only came with two. I stood at the end of her driveway looking for an area that could not be seen by anyone. For the first camera I installed I ran the cord up the downspout of her guttering. I placed the camera right on the edge of her roof facing the driveway, high angle looking down. The second camera was placed right in the middle of a bush facing the middle of the driveway, catching both vehicles on camera. Both cameras were hidden perfectly to catch Billy.

When I turned on the monitor, I could see all the way to the neighbor's house across the street; this was perfect coverage. I ran the wiring along the ground, covered with mulch and into the garage, then into Tammy's bar area of the house where the television would be on twenty-four hours a day with the volume turned up so we could hear any noises outside. I had to think like Billy at this point, which wasn't hard to do. He would return; when, I didn't know.

I drove up to Walmart to picked up five extended play VHS tapes. They would record up to eight hours. I was feeling good now. The bait was there; I just had to wait for the bite.

After hooking everything up, I asked Tammy to walk outside to the end of her driveway, then walk around our vehicles to make sure I had the coverage. After I had everything set, I walked out to meet her. I was pleased with the coverage I had.

Tammy asked, "Where are the cameras?"

I said, "Look for them." As Tammy there stood looking, she raised her hands in the air.

Tammy said, "I don't see them. Point them out to me."

I pointed up to where the cameras were. She had to look hard to see them, even with me pointing to them. They were small and didn't have any lights on them so that you couldn't see them in the dark watching you.

Tammy said, "Billy will see those, he is good at looking for things like that!"

I said, "Bullshit, Tammy, he cannot see the cameras. What is your freaking problem? Do you think Billy is smarter than I am, because that's what it sounds like to me? Is Billy some kind of superhero to you? Look this man has messed with my things, now I'll show him who the smart one is. You just watch."

Later that afternoon I walked across the street before dark to talk with the neighbors. I needed to ask them to keep their porch light on to help my cameras with lighting in the background.

Neighbors said they'd do anything to help catch Billy. They said he was mean and scared their children. They told me I was the best boyfriend Tammy has ever had, and they really liked me. "Tammy needed to find someone good like you. There is always something going with the police involved a lot with their fighting.

"When Tammy's oldest daughter Linda was younger, she'd walk the streets causing problems with all the neighbors, cutting through their yards. Tammy has had men in and out of there at all hours of the night," they said.

I couldn't believe my ears at what they were telling me about Tammy. I was starting to wonder if Tammy really was who she said she was. Maybe I needed to close my heart some and open my eyes more to what's going on here.

A week went by. I played the tape, which recorded during the night, every morning. I was hoping Billy would be on there doing something stupid. I walked out every morning making a visual check of our vehicles. I put the tape in every night around midnight, then hit extended play for 8 hours, hoping everything was recorded until I woke up the next morning.

CHAPTER 26

The Car Fire

My brother called me September 16th and told me he was leaving for Joplin, Missouri.

"I left the remote on your table for the television," he said.

"Ok, I'll stop by and get it sometime this week," I said, "but I want you to call me when you get to Joplin tonight. I don't care what time it is. I just want to know you made it there safely."

Tammy and I were sound asleep when my phone rang. I rolled over to answer it.

"Hello," I said.

Hey, Jim, I just called to tell you I made it to Joplin," he said.

"What time is it?' I asked.

"It's 2:45 am," he said. "I'm going to get into my truck and get some sleep before leaving out in the morning. They are sending me to the east coast."

"Ok, have a safe trip," I said. "I'll see you when you get back," hung up the phone, and closed my eyes.

"Was that your brother," she asked.

"Yes, he made it to Joplin all right," I said. "Sorry if I woke you up."

I fell back to sleep again. All of the sudden I was awakened by a punch to the chest at 3 am.

I sat up quickly and said, "What!" I was scared to death, not knowing who or what hit me, and why.

Tammy yelled, "My alarm!"

I said, "What?" still half asleep.

Tammy said, "My car alarm is going off."

I looked toward the front door. In the side window, I could see a glow of light, a bright glow shining through the glass. My first thought was there was someone here with their head lights shining into the house. I jumped out of bed and I ran up the stairs half way to look out the window. I couldn't believe my eyes or what I saw out there in the driveway.

"Tammy, your car is on fire!" I said with panic in my voice. "It's fully engulfed."

Tammy told me to run outside and grab a garden hose to put the fire out.

"Tammy, are you crazy? Billy is probably waiting out there for me. Call the fire department, Tammy! Hurry!" I said. As the flames got bigger, I could see another car behind hers.

"Tammy, whose car is behind yours?" I asked.

"What car?" she asked.

"There's a car behind your car, Tammy," I said. "Whose car is it?"

"I don't know whose car is out there," she said.

All I know is when Tammy and I went to bed, there were only two vehicles in the driveway, Tammy's car and my truck. Now I was starting to panic, all I could think about was Billy outside somewhere. Maybe that was his car parked behind Tammy's car, and Billy was waiting for us to come outside. Billy could be watching through a window, and he could be at any door ready to kick it in and kill me. I ran down the stairs and stood in the middle of her house, which gave me one of three doors to escape if I needed to. I was scared to death. I stood there waiting for something to happen.

Right then I wasn't in control of my life. I felt trapped inside Tammy's house with nowhere to run or hide.

'Tammy, did you call the Fire Department?" I yelled with fear in my voice.

"Yes, I did, Jim. And your truck is on fire too!"

At the time I didn't care about my truck; my life was more important. I was waiting for something to happen. I stood there looking at every window and door, wondering which one Billy was going to enter through. I glanced at the television taping the whole thing. I could see Tammy's car completely burning in a big ball of fire. I knew I had Billy's ass if I made it out of this alive. This time Billy would be on tape.

I could see a fire truck pulling up front, thanks to the security cameras. I watched a fireman walk up and knock on the door, which Tammy opened. I walked over to the door where they were.

The fireman asked, "Did you know your car was on fire?"

"Who do you think called you guys?" I asked, In a sarcastic frightened voice. I was quite uncomfortable with what happened. I've never been through something like this before. I'd really thought I was going to die in Tammy's house.

It took the fireman about fifteen minutes to put Tammy's car out. By then my truck had burned out. This time the police were there to see what was going on to make out a report. Finally, I felt safe, I could breathe normally again.

I told the officer we had no idea whose car was behind Tammy's car in the driveway.

The officer walked out to the car and ran the license plate on the car. He came back to tell us it belongs to Linda Simmons.

"Tammy, why is Linda's car here?" I asked.

"Oh, I forgot Linda called," she said. Linda told me she was going to leave it here after her boyfriend's softball game because he had been drinking. She wanted to leave her car here then drive her boyfriend home in his car."

That's what happens when you drink a box of wine after work. You forget who you talked with or what was said. Tammy was so calm like this was an everyday thing at her house. Her car burning didn't seem to faze her at all.

The policeman asked if we knew who did this to our vehicles.

"Yes, we do," I said. "Billy Wolf did this. I have Billy on tape, this time."

"You do?" the officer asked.

"Yes I do," I said with joy in my voice. I was safe now. Finally, I caught Billy in the act. I was so happy I'd be sending Billy away for a long time. Now I could be with the woman of my dreams, not worrying about Billy's after dark craziness anymore. I was so sure I had Billy on tape I wanted to ask Tammy "Who's the smart one now?"

I said with a big smile, "Let me get the tape out of the recorder. We'll have to play it in the master bedroom."

The policeman and Tammy waited in her bedroom until I came in with the tape. I was grinning from ear to ear as I came in, tape in hand. As soon as I played this tape they'd go to Billy's house and arrest him for arson and everything else he has done to us the past few months.

I put the tape in and rewound it for a bit. I hit play, and all we saw were moths flying and cricket sounds with both vehicle sitting quietly in the driveway.

"Hold on, let me rewind it some more," I said. I'm starting to panic! We're seeing nothing on the tape but moths flying in front of my cameras.

"I can't believe this," I said aloud. "This is an 8hr tape; I put it in at midnight. Billy has to be on here!"

Then it hit me like a ton of bricks, the remote! I needed the remote to record long play. It was only recording two hours on an eight-hour tape without the remote. How could this happen? I'd had Billy this time. I failed to pick up the remote my brother left at my house. I was so embarrassed to make such a fuss about having Billy on tape. Now I could only hang my head in defeat this time. I felt like sticking my head in the toilet and flushing it.

The fire marshall was outside inspecting the damage to our vehicles. I walked outside to see the damage done Tammy's car and my truck, but it was dark out. I couldn't see much of anything. Neither could the fire marshall.

The fire marshall said he'd be back around 8:00 a.m. to look at the vehicles and make out his report. He told Tammy to call her insurance company to report it so they could send out a fire inspector to access the damage.

Everyone left Tammy's house around 5 am. Tammy and I just stood outside looking at her car in disbelief at what Billy had done. The smell of the burnt car was horrible. There was black soot tracked all the way back to the front door. Billy was doing this while I was talking to my brother on the phone. If I had gotten up, I would have seen him doing it.

"It's 6 am; I'm going back to bed," she said. Tammy was as calm as a cucumber.

"Why are you going back to bed?" I asked. "How can you just go back to bed after all of this? What the hell is wrong with you, Tammy? Nothing Billy does bothers you."

"It's too early to call anyone," she said. "I'll do it when I get up."

What was wrong with her? What's going through her mind? How can she go back to bed after her car has been burned to the ground?

Something's not right here, I thought. Tammy was too calm about what had taken place this morning. Nothing Billy did seem to surprise Tammy at all. She didn't even apologize for the damage Billy did to my truck.

CHAPTER 27

The Gun Shot

Tammy jumped under her blankets and went back to sleep like nothing ever happened! I laid down at the foot of the bed watching the news until it was time to get up and make calls to her insurance company. I was still afraid Billy might still be close by. I didn't want to fall asleep. I bet Billy was down the street the whole time watching Tammy's car burn.

As I laid there watching the news, I dosed off. I was awakened immediately by a gun shot in my ear. I popped my head up to look around. I thought I had just been shot in the head. It scared me to death; it was real. I looked up at Tammy, who was sound asleep.

Something was not right about this. I needed to call Devonna. I had to find out why that gun shot went off inside my head to wake me up. Was that a sign to warn me? To warn me of what, I wondered.

The fire marshall, John, returned like he said he would at 8 am. I wanted to hear what John's thoughts were on how the cars were started on fire. I had my own ideas after looking at Linda's car. I could see Linda's car fire was started above the front tire in the thick plastic inner fender. It couldn't have been started with a cigarette lighter.

I waited to see what the fire marshal had to say about how it was started. John really didn't have a clue what Billy used to start the fire under Linda's fender. But I did and wanted to share my thoughts on it.

I pointed out to John, thick plastic like this. Billy had to use one of those butane torches plumbers use. That's the only thing which would get hot enough to start the thick plastic on fire.

John said, "I think you're right, Jim."

"I know I'm right, John," I said. "I do construction. I have two or three of them in my trailer. I use them for soldering copper together on plumbing jobs."

Looking at my truck, I saw Billy had started my brake line on fire in the middle of the rubber line. It would only burn as the brake fluid would drip on the flame. The fluid put the out fire by dripping on the flame because the flame was too small. Brake fluid isn't really flammable. Billy had to use a torch to start that rubber brake line. Using a torch was the only way Billy could have started all the vehicles on fire at the same time, giving him enough time to get away before it got too big. That's all the damage done to my truck. I figured a brake line for $40.00, not worth calling my insurance company. But enough to kick Billy's ass if I ever saw him in person.

After John had done his report, we talked a bit in Tammy's driveway.

I asked John if he knew my son, Chad Edwards who was in the Fireman's Academy in Broken Arrow.

"Yes, I do know your son," John said. "He will make a great fireman one day."

I was glad to hear that about my son. John was one of the trainers at the academy, and he saw Chad every day during training drills.

John asked me in private, "Have you ever thought about getting away from Tammy?"

I replied, "There is just something about her, John, which keeps me here. I really care about Tammy. Even though my kids don't like her very much. They don't know anything about what's been going on here at Tammy's house. I just want Billy to go away and let me take care of Tammy. She'll be all right after Billy is gone. The things Billy has been doing to Tammy has her all confused about everything. The poor girl is a mess. This is getting personal with me John. Billy has messed with both of my vehicles now."

Tammy walked up as John and I were standing in front of her car talking.

"Billy will never stop loving me!" she exclaimed.

I just wanted to die. I couldn't believe what came out of Tammy's mouth. I pointed to her car in anger.

"This is love? Is this what you call love? Open your freaking eyes, Tammy! Let me tell you what love is!" I shouted with anger. "Love is sending you flowers or candy, writing little notes, and putting them around the house. Love is never having to say you're sorry. Love is holding hands in public, cuddling on the couch, counting the stars together at night. That's love, Tammy! What the hell is wrong with you?"

Tammy just stood there looking stupid in her embarrassment. She was waiting for attention from both John and me. But instead, she heard me loudly voicing my opinion on what love really is.

John just looked at the frustration on my face. He laid his hand on my shoulder and told me to be careful. He then walked back to his car and left.

CHAPTER 28

Phone Calls

After John left, Tammy went in to start making her calls. She called her insurance man first. It seemed Tammy and Billy share the same insurance man, doctor, and tax man.

I asked Tammy if she and Billy were married.

Tammy said, "No, we are not married. Billy needed help after his divorce. I told Billy I would help him get started."

I said, "You are living like husband and wife. With both of your names on everything. That's what married people do, Tammy."

I was really confused who the boyfriend was. Billy is still around, and I was here with Tammy, who calls me her boyfriend at this time. Who knows, tomorrow it maybe Billy again.

Tammy called Billy's probation officer, Joy Smith, to ask Joy if she had heard what Billy has been doing. Tammy told Joy everything which had been done to her for the past month.

Joy told Tammy, "Billy said he wrecked his green truck, and now he has a 2007 black Avalanche without plastic trim.

Billy also asked for a pass to go to Arizona for a week with a lady friend. Billy was to return home Friday night, the night your car was set on fire." Joy told Tammy Billy had lost his job with the oil company before going to Arizona.

Tammy said, "That's not good news, I've been sending the police after Billy's green truck. I had no idea Billy bought a new truck or lost his job."

After hanging up the phone with Joy, Tammy said, "I'm pissed; Billy knew I wanted one of those trucks. That's why he bought it. He thinks he can get me back with that truck."

"Right, Tammy!" I said. "Billy bought the truck so he could do what he has been doing while his green truck is sitting in his driveway. I bet Billy still has a paper tag on it not registered in his name yet. The reason Billy bought a different truck is so he could drive by your house during the day to plan his next move. A black truck cannot be seen during the night in a dark area."

I was getting tired of hearing Tammy talk about how smart Billy was. To get a different truck, to pull his capers during the night so he won't get caught. I had a feeling Tammy was still in love with this weirdo. We had been arguing a lot over Billy's crap, and this would be the test if we'd make it. I was starting to wonder if it was Tammy's way of playing a game with Billy, and I was the middle man in their game.

I told Tammy, "I was going to call Devonna tonight to find out what Billy's plans are. When will Billy come again? Will I be ready for him? What is Billy going to do next? I have a lot of thinking to do. Things have been escalating out of control lately."

Later that night, I stepped out back to make my call to Devonna.

I told Devonna about Billy burning Tammy's car. I wanted to know if I was in any danger. I told Devonna a gunshot woke me up after I dosed off this morning.

"Devonna," I asked, "was that a warning shot for me? What's going on?"

Devonna said as she was looking at my cards, "Be careful, Jim. The gun shot was a warning. Billy is coming after you; I don't know when, but he is coming. I also see the next card shows Billy fails to get you. I see this man is held hostage in a house, thinking about killing himself, but he gives up to the police."

I told Devonna I loved her and thanked her for the update on Billy's plans to hunt me down. I would be more careful from now on.

Tammy asked, "What did Devonna have to say?"

I told Tammy, "Devonna said Billy was coming after me, but he fails to get me."

"That woman doesn't know crap," Tammy said. "I told you Billy said he would kill me if I broke up with him again. Billy is coming after me."

"Yeah, ok Tammy," I said. "Keep talking, because in June when we talked with Devonna about Billy, you were all about hearing the news about him going to jail in November of this year. When Devonna told us about Billy, you weren't surprised at all to hear how bad he was. Devonna told us what you already knew about Billy. Now it's up to me to catch Billy in the act."

CHAPTER 29

Seeing Billy

"Sometime between now and November I need to be on my guard," I said, "watching my back. I'm just the boyfriend in all of this. Tammy, you assured me Billy would go away in time, that he'd find someone else and leave us alone. I'm starting feel like my life is in danger. I'm going to catch Billy with or without you before he hurts someone really badly."

I would no longer be hunted by Billy. From now on, I will be the hunter, looking for him. I'll watch for Billy around the clock. From this day on, I'd start thinking like Billy. Where's Billy going to enter the house from? I'll do my best to have traps ready for him when he comes back next time.

If Billy was coming for Tammy, like she said he would, I'd be here to save her from him, if I could. I'm not going to die for Tammy. But I think she is saying that for my attention right now.

"From now on, Tammy," I said, "I'll take naps during the day if I can. I'll stay up as long as I can, waiting for Billy. By messing with my vehicle, he has involved me personally. It's a mission of mine now I catch Billy and send him away for good, and you'll be there to see it."

Lori came home from school later that afternoon. She had spent the night with a friend. When Lori saw Tammy's car burned in the driveway, she started crying.

Lori said, "Billy has taken my cat, and burned your car, Mom! I'm tired of Billy destroying our things. I hate Billy," she said as she went running up to her room.

I felt so sorry for Lori. She was such a good girl, never causing problems, but living with her mother's stupid decisions. Lori was embarrassed in front of her friends. She lived with the drama and turmoil Tammy and Billy caused throughout their relationship.

For days we smelled that nasty burned car in the driveway. The neighborhood association stopped by to ask that we cover the car with a tarp until Tammy's insurance company had it towed off. The hot September sun was making it smell so bad you could even smell it with the doors shut to the house.

Tammy's ex-husband Edward stopped over. He stood over Tammy's car. Edward said, "I cannot believe Billy did this. This has gone too far now. Lori cannot stay here anymore unless you stay Jim. I want to make sure Lori is safe here."

"Edward, I'll stay at the house to make sure Lori is safe so she could sleep in her bed at night. I would protect her if Billy came back over to the house."

After Edward left, I sat out in the driveway in a lawn chair. I was in deep thought. What was Billy going do next, and what was I going to do to catch Billy? Whatever it was, I had to be ready for it. I was just staring into space enjoying the nice weather and the sound of silence.

I turned my head left, looking down the street, and saw Billy parked at the corner in a black truck, just staring up at Tammy's house and tarp-covered car. I jumped up from my chair and started walking toward the end of the driveway to get a better look at Billy. Billy saw me looking his way and hit the gas, speeding off down the street in his black Avalanche pickup.

I went into the house and told Tammy about Billy being down at the corner in a black truck.

"Are you sure it was Billy?" she asked.

"Yes, it was Billy," I said. "He's not supposed to be within 500 yards of you or your house. Call the police; let's make out a report. We have to make out reports every time Billy does something. That's the documentation we'll need Tammy."

A police car showed up, they took a report, and once again there was nothing they could do because I was the only one who saw Billy.

"Next time, try and get a picture with your phone," the officer said.

"He drives a 2007 Black Avalanche," I said. "Can't you just look into the GPS on the truck and see where Billy has been the past few weeks? Then you would have your man."

"We can't do that sir, but that would be the easy way to catch him," he said. "But the law keeps us from doing things like that unless it's a murder case or worse."

It didn't make sense. With all the reports we have filed against Billy, you'd think they'd look into it. Nothing was being done, and that was what bothers me the most. I was on my own catching Billy. The police weren't doing their job with all the reports filed, and Tammy wasn't helping much.

CHAPTER 30

The Gun

A couple of days later, Tammy's daughter, Linda, brought over a gun from Edward. It was a 1927 Smith and Wesson six-shooter.

"My dad gave this to you for protection, just in case Billy shows up again," she said.

I've never shot a gun before. I didn't really know the first thing about shooting it. This gun was so old I wonder if it would even shoot. I took it into the house and laid it on the nightstand in Tammy's bedroom.

Now things had escalated to having a gun by the bedside. I'm just the boyfriend here, not a security guard. I'm pretty sure this is not in the boyfriend's rule book. I was in too deep now. I had to catch Billy. He knew where I was living.

I heard through the grapevine John the fire marshall thought we set our own vehicles on fire because my security system didn't record the fire. This was not good news, not what I wanted to hear. Why would they think we started our own vehicles on fire when they were paid off? Everyone keeps making excuses to keep from doing their job. Once again, I was on my own here.

Tammy's insurance company sent out their fire investigator, who was going to be able to tell if the car was started deliberately by us and how it was started. He was good. He showed me things, like how the fire rings on the metal, showed him where it was started, then started a second time. He showed John some things which changed John's mind about us starting our own fire. This was a peace of mind for me but wasn't going to help us have Billy arrested for starting the fires.

The four of us stood by Tammy's car. The insurance investigator told Tammy he would have it removed by the weekend.

Tammy started telling her story about the things Billy has done to her, with her poor pity look. She told them that she loaned Billy $10,000.00 to get out of trouble when he came last year with a gun. Tammy said, "Billy owes me that money, I'll take him to court if I have to."

Tammy was looking for some attention again, while telling her sad story about Billy. However, they knew Tammy dropped the charges to get Billy off last year.

The investigator said, "I have seen this kind of thing before. Let me tell you guys something, just live your normal lives. Guy's like Billy mean no threat. He just made a statement he's still around. So just live your normal lives. He is no harm to you at all."

I couldn't believe what I was hearing from this man, live our normal life and don't worry after Billy set three vehicles on fire and done other things to us. He's not going through this, so it's easy for him to tell us not to worry and live normally.

The investigator said, "Men like Billy always get caught. They think they can get away with things, but they always get caught."

After they had left, I asked Tammy why she told them she loaned Billy money to get out of trouble. "You know they really don't care about Billy owing you money, or your relationship with him. That's why they thought we started the fires, to get your money back from insurance. To pay your credit cards off. You say things without thinking, Tammy, that's what gets you into trouble all the time."

CHAPTER 31

The Stake Outs

For some reason, I started getting the feeling Tammy thought she was every man's dream girl. I think she loves the drama and turmoil in all of this. The attention she is receiving puts her on center stage in her mind. She's always butting in on other people's business, giving them advice when Tammy cannot control what goes on in her life. Why would she give others advice? Why would they even listen to her? I'm starting to wonder if she liked playing the poor innocent damsel in distress just for the attention with no intentions of breaking up Billy for good. She is just waiting to see how far I'll go with this before leaving her.

Then it hit me.

"I've done everything your way up till now," I said. "Ever since I've started coming to your house, I've been trapped here, and we never go anywhere anymore. Why is that, Tammy?

"You haven't been back to my house since early August. Well, Tammy," I said, "the shoe is on the other foot now! We are going to do things my way, or I'm done being your boyfriend, plain and simple. It's your call."

"What do you have in mind?" she asked.

"From now on, I'll not be hunted by Billy, I'll be the hunter. I'm a lot smarter than he is. I'll catch him one day."

"Tell me what you are going to do," she inquired.

"What 'we' are going to do Tammy," I said, "is do this together. Not just me! Both of us, unless you don't want to catch Billy."

"Don't be silly," she said. Tammy was having fun with the attention she was getting.

"Follow me, Tammy." I took her out the side door from the garage. I said, "Billy will jump this fence and hide. You cannot be seen back in this corner, and Billy will use it. I will lay plywood down on the ground with 16 penny nails sticking up through it so when Billy jumps off the fence. The nails will go through his feet. I will cover it with leaves so Billy cannot see it. It will hurt! Billy will scream."

I pointed to the door we just walked out of. "Billy will come through that door, or try to, even though I have a dead bolt on it now. Billy can kick it in, but I'm going to place this shovel under the handle like this. He can kick as much as he wants to. Billy will have to break the frame to get in. By then, he will be heard by us or the neighbors. Believe me, Tammy, Billy will come to this door."

Tammy just followed me, not saying a word. She just listened to what I had carefully planned to catch Billy. I gave this a lot of thought. My plan was full proof. Someone like Billy is a coward. He will hide, then sneak up on me when I'm not looking.

Next, I took Tammy into her bedroom. "Tammy, if Billy enters the house, I will keep him on the other end of the house by shooting at him with the gun Edward gave me to protect

Lori. Then I want you to open your window, knock out the screen, step outside, and leave through your gate to the front yard to call the police. Then I will meet you out front. Can you do that, Tammy?"

Tammy said, "Yes, I can do that, but how are you going to get out?"

"I will jump out through the bathroom window. Then I will meet you out front. We will hide until the police get here. That's my plan on how to catch Billy, and it will work."

Tammy was ok with the shovel keeping the door shut. She didn't want me to use the plywood with nails to catch Billy.

"Jim, I don't want to hurt Billy," she said. "Just catch him, that's all." She acted like this was a game. Catch Billy if you can, is what she meant.

"Well, Tammy why don't I just stand on the roof and drop a net on Billy, so I don't hurt him?" Then I got angry, thinking about what Tammy had just said. "You know what, if I had a freaking bear trap, Tammy, I'd set it for Billy's ass."

"Tammy, we have figured out Billy comes between 2 am and 4 am right after the bar closes. So from this day on we'll rest during the day as much as we can, staying up during the nights hiding out. We'll do this until Billy is caught. Since your boss is letting you do your work from home now, you can rest some during the day and help me watch during the night.

"What do you mean, hideout?" she asked.

"Tonight after dark, I will go outside to look for the darkest spots I can find," I said, places where Billy cannot see us watching for him. That's where we'll be waiting for Billy to show up again. When we see Billy coming down the street, we call the police. We'll stay there until they arrest him and haul Billy away."

"What time is this going to take place?" she asked.

"Starting at midnight we will be out waiting for Billy to show up," I said.

"Why outside?" she asked.

"Because, Tammy, I'm in more control of my life outside. I have no control inside your house. No telling what Billy might do next time; he may throw fire bottles through your windows while we are sleeping. Billy seems to like fire. Billy will be waiting for us to come running outside. So it's my way Tammy, or I'm going home, and you can deal with Billy alone. That's my final offer to you as your boyfriend!"

"Ok!" she said raising her voice in frustration.

I knew this wasn't going to be easy. I was calling Tammy at her own bluff. Tammy was going to be hard to deal with, let's see how badly she wanted to catch Billy. I told Tammy she needed to go to bed around 10:00 pm because I'd wake her up around midnight so that we could hide out.

The nights were hard for me since the car burning. I hated it when the sun went down. I had a great plan to keep us safe. I tried to rely on my inner feelings about what to do, and when to do it. I guess if I really listened to my inner intuitions, I would have left Tammy after my jeep was fixed. But now my mission was to catch Billy Wolf.

I tried waking Tammy up at midnight, but she moaned and groaned until I said, "Get up now or I'm leaving!" She finally got out of bed at 12:45, bitching the whole time. My patience was growing thin. I was already full of fear Billy was already here. I could hear my heart beating inside my chest and was getting angry with Tammy for taking her time. I managed to hold in my frustrations while she got out of bed.

I said, "Hurry up, Tammy. Wear all black please."

Tammy asked, "Why do I need to wear black?"

"So Billy can't see us, that's why. Now hurry, please! My mind is putting me into a panic mode telling me Billy is out there already."

Tammy started packing a bag after getting dressed.

"What are you doing, Tammy?"

"I'm getting some snacks, flashlight, and lip gloss," she said. Then she wanted me to get some lawn chairs to sit on.

"We're not going on a picnic, Tammy! Hurry, please!" My heart was beating even louder with anxiety running through my body, and fear was taking over.

"Where are we going to be tonight?" she asked

"Tonight, Tammy, we are on the roof."

"I don't want to be on the roof; I'm afraid of heights," she said.

"Well, tonight you will be with me up on the roof. This way we can see both ends of the street. If Billy comes walking from either end, we call the police, they catch him, and we never have to do this again. Now, let's go. The roof is waiting for us."

It wasn't going to be easy getting Tammy on the roof, or any place we needed to be looking for Billy. Tammy lasted thirty minutes before she started complaining about not being comfortable. Her roof wasn't steep at all. She could just lay there, sleeping for all I care. It would be a lot easier on me if she would. This way I could watch for Billy without being bothered by Tammy's complaining.

"How much longer?" she asked.

"We've only been here for thirty minutes Tammy," I said.

"How long are we going to be here tonight?" she asked.

"Until 4 am Tammy."

"What?" she said loudly.

"Keep it down I," whispered loudly. Tammy then started moving around, asking every five minutes asking what time it was. I was shaking my head, thinking to myself she is going to get me killed. Billy could have heard Tammy just then and started shooting at us, or something.

"I'm slipping off the roof," she said.

"You are not slipping, Tammy! Now lay your head on the ridge and go to sleep; I'll wake you up when it is time to go in."

Tammy slapped her hand on the roof, "Billy is not coming tonight. Let's go in. I'm tired. I wanna sleep in my bed."

"Tammy, I've had just about all I'm going to take from you tonight!" I looked at her. "Either you shut up and help me watch for Billy, or you can take your happy ass in your house. I'll go to my house where I can get some sleep. I'm only doing this because I love you. I'm trying to protect you and Lori. If this is too much for you to handle, we can call it quits right now. I'll get my things and go home. Because this is starting to wear me down."

"What are you saying to me?" she asked.

"Look, Tammy, this is your old boyfriend making this impossible for us to have a normal relationship. Billy is the reason we are up here tonight. If it were an old girlfriend of mine, you would have been gone a long time ago. Now, Tammy, you can help me catch Billy without any bloodshed, or I'm leaving for good.

"Tammy it's 4:30 am, I guess Billy's not coming tonight. See how time flies when you act right? So today you need to get plenty of rest, because tonight we will be out again, in a different spot." Being on the roof, I was able to look for good spots to hide out.

"I have to work today!" she said.

"I have work too, Tammy. But I'll be here to do it again tonight because that is the sacrifice I'm willing to make until Billy is caught."

With Tammy being able to work from home, it really worked out great for us. When we came in at 4:30 am, Tammy could sleep until 10:00 am before clocking in for work. I was only getting three to four hours of sleep a day, not much at all, but I'd take what I could get until Billy was caught.

Every morning I left Tammy's house at 6 am. I'd return around 4 pm from work and lay down until 6 pm while Tammy was on watch. I really didn't sleep well if any at all. What would Tammy do if Billy showed up while I was sleeping? Would she tell me? Would she scream? Who knows what would happen. I could only hope Tammy would warn me if Billy had shown up. I had my doubts about Tammy though.

CHAPTER 32

Meeting the Parents

I met a couple of parents whose daughter was Lori's friend. They stopped by to see what Billy did to Tammy's car. They knew Tammy and Billy from their daughter, who spent the night on occasion with Lori. Curious to meet Tammy's new boyfriend, they wanted to talk with me about being Billy and Tammy's next victim. I was all ears; I could use all the information I could get.

Their daughter was here last year spending the night with Lori when Billy showed up with a gun at 3 am. They told me their daughter hid in the closet upstairs with Lori. Their daughter had called them, scared to death crying and begging for them to come to get her. She told her parents Billy was there with a gun, and he was going to shoot Tammy.

Bob, her father, told me they tried to get to the house, but every cop from Broken Arrow was there with their guns drawn. He told me when they arrested Billy, the police threw Billy to the ground and cuffed him.

"What pissed me off was," he said, "Tammy standing there yelling at the police not to hurt Billy. Over and over she was yelling, "Don't hurt him.'

"I was so mad at Tammy, I wanted to punch her in the mouth," he said.

Bob's wife, Sarah, told me she wanted to scratch Tammy's eyes out for protecting Billy.

Sarah told me that her daughter was hiding in a closet right above where Billy was standing that night. If he'd shot the gun up into the ceiling, he would have hit one of the girls. "We didn't talk to Tammy for six months after that night, nor did we let our daughter stay the night with Lori anymore. I know it's not Lori's fault, it's her mother's fault in all of this. Tammy keeps protecting Billy."

"Tammy begged us for weeks not to press charges on Billy," she said. "Tammy was at the station bright and early the next morning to see Billy. Now look at what Billy's has done," looking at Tammy's burned car in the driveway, "because Tammy asked us not to press charges," she said.

"If I could do it all over again, I'd put Billy away for a long time."

Then Sarah said, "If I were you, Jim, I'd run. Get away from Tammy and Billy because he's crazy and Tammy will protect Billy. You're nothing but their next victim in their crazy games."

"Sarah, do you think it's just Billy having control over Tammy?" I asked. "Maybe Tammy is really afraid of Billy, that's why she is helping him."

"Tammy loves Billy," Sarah said. "I don't know what Tammy see's in Billy, but she loves him enough to protect him.

You are only here until Billy runs you off, then they'll be back together again, doing the same thing with someone different.

"Billy is not going to run me off, Sarah; Billy has messed with both of my vehicles. Now it's personal, and I'll catch him being stupid again, and send him away for good."

After my visit with Bob and Sarah, it gave me a better idea of who both Billy and Tammy were. I mentioned to Tammy what they had to say about the whole ordeal with Billy last year, and I asked why Tammy asked the police not to hurt Billy.

"Yes, I did say that," she said. "I felt like Billy needed counseling."

"Did Billy seek counseling, Tammy?" I asked.

"Hell no! As soon as court was over, Billy changed back into an asshole again."

"So, in other words, you got your $10,000.00 you gave Billy to get out of his mess? Now take a look at the mess you are in. Billy won't go away until he gets caught. Believe me, Tammy, Billy will get caught eventually."

"I was raised to believe there is good in everyone," she said.

"News flash, Tammy! There's not good in everyone. Most people will only tell you what you want to hear to get what they need. Now you have $10,000.00 to pay back to your credit card, plus the $500.00 I loaned you for your air-conditioning, and you don't have a car anymore.

"I'm getting my money back from Billy," she said, "even if I have to take Billy to court. The only reason Billy burned the car up is because he bought it for me with part of the $10,000.00 I gave him to get out of trouble. When I met you,

I talked Billy into signing it over to me, that pissed him off. That's why Billy burned thc car."

"Now the finger is pointed at me?" I asked. "It's my fault your car was torched by Billy? Because I'm here is why Billy is doing this. I'm here because you broke up with Billy and promised me he'd go away and leave us alone."

"I didn't say that," she said

"You just did Tammy," I said, "by asking Billy to sign the title over to you after you met me. So I'm the reason for Billy's actions against you."

Maybe I should leave like Bob and Sarah told me to. Billy was crazy, and Tammy seems to be protecting him. But Billy cut the wiring on my Jeep, and he tried to setting my truck on fire. Now it was personal.

I'm not sure if this is a love story anymore. I'd protect Tammy, though, if it came to that, but the stress she is giving me protecting Billy's actions is wearing thin on me. I won't rest until Billy is caught.

Tonight's hideout took us across the street behind some bushes which lined the neighbor's house. There was a tall privacy fence, surrounded with bushes planted two feet from the fence. It was very dark in that corner. Hiding behind the bushes made it impossible for us to be seen. Being on the roof the night before, I was able to see this dark spot.

Tammy was in one of her moods as usual.

"Billy's not coming tonight," she said.

"Tammy, did you talk to Billy today? Did Billy tell you he wasn't coming tonight? Because he was tired and told you wc could take a break tonight and catch up on some sleep, instead of being out here tonight?"

"No, I haven't talked to Billy," she said. "If he is not here by now he's not coming. Billy has night vision goggles. He could be watching us right now for all we know!"

When Tammy said that, I just about threw my hands in the air and told Tammy she was on her own. Now I was feeling like a sitting duck, paranoid as hell. I lowered myself down, I crawled into the bushes, peeking out to see if Billy was out there watching us with his goggles on. I could hear my heart beating loudly in my chest.

"Tammy, is there anything else I should know about Billy?" I asked. "Does Billy fly? Can Billy leap over tall buildings?" I was getting angry with the crap she was saying to me. Billy was Tammy's hero. In her eyes, he could do no wrong.

Once again Billy didn't show up, but I wasn't going to stop my stakeouts because that's when he'd show up. Some nights I'd lay on the stairway with that old gun in my lap, looking out the window every fifteen minutes, or when I heard something out of the ordinary on the monitor just below me in the bar area. Tammy and Lori slept quietly in their beds throughout the night while I watched for Billy.

This way of living was starting to wear me down, affecting my moods, and my work too. It'd been almost two weeks since the car fire. I knew Billy would sneak back soon, but when? What was he going to do this time? If I just had a hint, I'd be ready for him.

I talked to Tammy's neighbor next door. His name was Jerry, and he told me about Billy always looking at him with evil eyes when he was out mowing his lawn. Jerry and I talked about his neighbors. It seemed the police had been over to Tammy's house quite often ever since she started dating Billy.

Jerry said, "They are always up until early hours of the morning. Billy would peel his tires in the street. You could hear them fighting all the time, all hours of the night until the police showed up. One day, Billy came over to Tammy's house, Billy ran his truck into a tree in front of Tammy's house, knocking it over onto the roof."

Jerry continued, "Billy is crazy. I keep two loaded shotguns in my house. If Billy ever comes into my yard, he is done for." He paused, "I like you, Jim, you are the best man Tammy has ever had around here. If I hear any gun shots over there, I'll come over with my shotgun. If you need to borrow it, just let me know."

It was good to know if Jerry heard any gunshots next door, he'd be right over to help me.

However, this gun talk was scaring me. I've never had a gun, never shot a gun, I really don't want a gun. But everyone thinks a gun solves everything. Whatever happened to bare knuckle fights, winner takes all?

So far Tammy's neighbors have reported to me there is always trouble at Tammy's house involving the police. Both neighbors have told me I was the best man Tammy has had around. Something is not right about all of this. Tammy's neighbors wouldn't just make up stories about Tammy and Billy.

What happened to the innocent beautiful woman I met five months ago, at the nursery surrounded by plants and flowers that beautiful day? The woman who I thought from our first hello would be my next forever? Who was Tammy? I was starting to have second thoughts about who Tammy said she was. I was going to finish what I started, catch Billy sending him away for good, or die trying.

Tonight's hideout was going to be at a motel. I needed some rest. My body and mind were about to drop dead. I couldn't stay up one more night looking out for Billy without a good night's sleep. Since Billy had the address to my house, I needed a safe place to sleep all night without any distractions.

"Tammy," I said, "we are staying at a motel tonight; I need some sleep."

"Why a motel?" she asked.

"Because Billy has my address now, and he can do whatever he wants tonight. I need sleep. Now grab an overnight bag and let's go find a motel."

"I can't leave all my animals here," she said. "Billy might burn my house down with all my animals in it."

"I don't think Billy is going to burn your house down, Tammy. Now grab a bag with some clothes, and let's get going and find a motel."

I finally talked Tammy into packing a bag so we could get a good night's sleep in a motel. After packing her bag, Tammy walked around the house saying goodbye to each one of her animals.

We got into the Jeep and were finally on our way to find a motel close to Tammy's house. I've lived in Tulsa thirty-five years, but I seemed to forget where all the motels were, so I drove around what seemed like forever looking for one.

"You know Billy could be following us," she said.

"Are you kidding me, Tammy?" I asked. "What the hell is wrong with you? Here you go again; Billy is the smart one because he hasn't been caught yet. Do me a favor, Tammy, from now on keep your comments about Billy to yourself."

I started driving faster, turning down roads to see if someone was following me in my Jeep. I was getting pissed. Every time I did something Tammy would tell me Billy was outsmarting me. After two hours of driving around looking for a motel, I drove into Tulsa because I knew where a few places were right off the highway. I didn't care. It was almost 10 pm, and I needed some sleep. Billy could do whatever he wanted to my Jeep tonight, but I was getting some sleep.

We checked into an Embassy Suites for the night. I dropped onto the bed, ready to sleep until I woke, whenever that would be. Tammy was wide awake. She wanted to watch some television and fool around. I begged her to let me sleep, and if she wanted too in the morning, we could fool around before we checked out. I finally talked Tammy into leaving me be until morning.

Why is it when you get a motel room for the night your wife, a girlfriend or whoever wants to stay up all night and do it? We can do that at home. People usually get a motel room because they are tired and need a place to sleep, to recharge overnight.

We checked out at 10 am and headed back to Tammy's house to see if it was still standing or smoldering from a fire that Billy started. The house was fine. No sign of Billy last night either. I felt good after getting nine hours of solid sleep. My brain was recharged, along with my body.

CHAPTER 33

Keller Williams job

I received a call from Keller Williams asking me to bid on some work they needed to be done. It consisted of painting all the walls throughout the office building and installing new Formica on their counter tops. If I were to get the bid, I'd have to work nights after they closed at 5 pm.

I sold the job and knew it would take me a week to complete it. Working nights was wonderful, not sleeping on Tammy's stairway waiting for Billy to show up. Listening strange noises and looking out through the window into the driveway with a gun laying in my lap. This job would almost be a vacation for me.

Things went pretty smooth the last two weeks of September. Maybe Billy found someone else. That would be a peace of mind. I brought my Jeep over for Tammy to run her errands and take Lori to school since she had no car now. My jeep had to stay in the garage when Tammy wasn't driving it, with the garage door down. I was firm with my statement on my jeep being in the garage.

September 27th around 4:30 pm, Tammy's home phone rang. The caller ID showed Caller Unknown.

Tammy said, "It's Billy. He is calling again from a pay phone." She didn't answer the call. She just stared at the phone while it rang.

That was first time we heard from Billy since September 17th, the night he burned Tammy's car. No calls, nothing done outside during the night. Was that call one last effort to talk with Tammy? Was Billy saying goodbye for good this time? I could only hope so.

September 28th, Friday night, I finished painting all the walls. Everything was completed at Keller Williams except two pieces of Formica. I told Tammy I needed to finish the job before they opened Monday morning. I'd put the Formica on Saturday night and clean it up Sunday morning.

"Sunday is your birthday, Jim," she said, "I'm having a party for you, so you need to finish it Saturday."

"I can't finish it by myself Saturday, Tammy. the pieces are too big for me to handle alone. It will take me all day by myself to finish the job."

Tammy asked, "How about I help you install the Formica? Can I help you with it? Then I can have your birthday party Sunday. I invited your children and your sister over for a cookout and cake. Besides, I like doing that kind of work."

"Yeah, you can help me. It'll be fun having you there with me. You can see what I do for a living."

Saturday afternoon, Tammy and I went to Keller Williams after they closed around 3 pm to install the Formica on their counter tops. It's not an easy job installing Formica. We didn't finish the job until 11 pm that night. I had boxes sitting on the Formica to help hold it down until the adhesive dried.

Monday morning before they opened, I'd remove the boxes so they could use their countertops.

Tammy said, "Now you can have tomorrow off for your party." She was happy about that. She had planned a party for me, and now she could have it.

CHAPTER 34

Birthday Party

Sunday, September 30th, I turned 47. Tammy had big plans for me today. She invited my family over to join me on my birthday. First thing Tammy wanted to do was run to Walmart to get a few things for the party.

Tammy and I were holding hands, swinging them together as we walked into Walmart. We were so happy being together when Billy wasn't interfering. I just loved Tammy so much. Tammy took me over to the deli counter and made me stand there behind the long line of people waiting for service.

"Stay here, Jim, don't leave until you get me two pounds of smoked turkey. I'm going to get a few things. Come and find me when you're done," she said.

She was so happy that day, like it was her birthday. I stood there watching her walk away from me, pushing a cart looking back with a smile, to make sure I wasn't following her. I thought to myself as I watched her walk out of sight, "She is so beautiful, I love her so much." She has such a cute little walk about her. I wanted to spend the rest of my life with

Tammy. I hoped Billy was gone for good now. I was tired of his night time games.

I got the smoked turkey like Tammy told me to. Now the search was on, looking down each aisle searching for my girl-friend. I spotted Tammy in the bread aisle, with her back to me. So I picked up a loaf of hot dog buns, tossed them it hitting her in the back to get her attention. Tammy turned around smiling at me while calling me goofy.

Tammy asked, "Did you get the smoked turkey?"

I said, "Yes, honey, but it will cost you a kiss to get it." I grabbed Tammy in my arms I kissed her on the cheek. I felt so close to her, like everything was over with Billy and we could move forward together.

We paid for our groceries and the party supplies. Tammy tried keeping out of my view; she had them hidden under things in her shopping cart. We walked out to my truck, loaded the groceries into the back seat, and headed back to Tammy's house.

Tammy said, "You have to act surprised when your family shows up, I told them you didn't know anything about the party. Oh, one more thing, Jim, I need you to run over to your house and get your grill because we are having burgers and brats for your party."

When we got back to Tammy's house, we unloaded the groceries onto the counter. Something came over me; a feeling that I'd never had before since being with Tammy. I looked at Tammy then I grabbed her tightly in my arms. I looked deep into her eyes.

"I don't want to ever lose you!" I said, "Do you know that Tammy?"

Something came to me, for no reason at all, but I had to tell her that. Like my intuition was telling me something.

Tammy looked into my eyes. She asked, "Do you think I'm going to die or something?" Looking at me with concern in her eyes, like I knew something bad was going to happen to her.

"No, of course, you're not going to die," I said, "I just want to keep you forever, that's all."

The doorbell rang, I opened the door to find my daughter Paige standing there.

Paige said, "Happy birthday, dad. I love you," with a hug as she walked into the hous, and headed toward the kitchen, where Tammy was standing with a smile. I knew they were up to something.

I left to pick up the grill at my house. While I was gone, Paige and Tammy decorated the kitchen with streamers, balloons, and even a birthday chair for me. They were making such a big deal for me that day. I'd been through so much of Billy's crap, I needed a day off to enjoy family and friends.

My sister, Kaelonnie, and her husband, Tommy, showed up for the party. I was real close to my sister. She was my baby sister, but I kept almost everything Billy had been doing from her. I didn't want them to know anything. I'd take care of it by myself, not getting them involved or worried about me. This was the first time they had been to Tammy's house.

Tammy's kids didn't show up for my party. I thought that was strange since I was dating their mother. I guess in their eyes I was just the boyfriend. Who shows up for the boyfriend's birthday party?

I had a wonderful birthday party that day. My family stayed until 10 pm. We even had a fire going in Tammy's fire pit. We sat around the fire in lawn chairs talking, even after dark, with my family there. I was at ease, I forgot all about Billy. We never did eat any of the cake or sing Happy Birthday while sitting in my birthday chair. But we laughed, told stories and hugged that night. I couldn't have asked for a better birthday party.

After the last person had left Tammy handed me a birthday card. She wanted me to open it after everyone was gone. Inside the card, she wrote: "I want to spend the rest of my life pampering you." Those words meant everything to me after what I have been through the past five months with Billy's jealousy. I wasn't too sure how Tammy really felt about me before the card. I felt relaxed. I thought Billy was gone for good.

Tammy and I headed off to her bedroom to call it a night. I reminded Tammy I needed to be up by 6 am so I could clean up the mess at Keller Williams before they opened at 8 am.

"Ok I'll wake you up when I wake up at 6:00," she said.

"Perfect. Thank you so much for the party today I love you. See you in the morning,"

I kissed her on the cheek before rolling over.

That night I slept hard, the first time ever in Tammy's house. Not even waking up for a minute during the night. I was so tired. I went right to sleep. I was so relaxed I forgot about Billy. My guard was down for the first time in months. I felt so at ease I slept like a baby all night.

CHAPTER 35

The Shooting

October 1st. "Mom, it's 7:23, you need to get up. I have twenty minutes before school." That's what I heard Lori telling Tammy that morning, as I jumped up.

"I'm late, Tammy! I needed to be at Keller Williams by 7 am before they opened," I said. I leaned over and kissed Tammy on the cheek. "I'm going to start some coffee and have a smoke in the garage. I'll be right back."

I walked into the kitchen to let the dogs out, like I did every morning, but Lori had already done that. I noticed she left the kitchen door unlocked. I have preached to Lori about leaving any doors unlocked while Billy was doing crazy things to us. I'll tell Tammy after my smoke Lori needs to follow the rules about locking doors. I looked out the kitchen door window, to see the dogs. Roxie the boxer was laying on the trampoline and Tori was laying in the grass under the sun.

I thought to myself, "Billy never strikes during the day." I locked the door anyway, started some coffee, and made my way out to the garage for a smoke.

I lit a cigarette, then laid my cell phone and smokes on the work bench. I took a drag off of my cigarette. I heard a noise; sounded like scratching on the door. I knew the gate was left open to the side yard from the party last night. I figured the dogs wanted in the garage with me. I'd let them in with me before, they'd just snoop around until I put them back out.

I laid my cigarette down, removed the shovel from under the door knob, unlocked the deadbolt and doorknob, pulling open the door expecting to find the dogs standing there.

I found myself standing there looking into a pair of black eyes, with a gun being raised to my head. Many thoughts were racing through my mind. "Am I going to die right here, Mom?" was the first thought to myself.

Billy was dressed all in black, and his face was almost covered by the black ski mask he was wearing. Black gloves, black gun, and black eyes to match. Billy had no soul in his eyes. He just stared at me, not even blinking. I was waiting for the gun to go off into my head. I was searching for a plan. I had to act quickly or die standing there at the door.

I was still holding the door knob with my right hand. Billy was only inches from me, with the gun almost touching my forehead. I could see inside the barrel of the gun. "Oh God," I said as I pushed the door back toward Billy, stepping to the side. I dropped to my knees, locking my hands around the doorknob.

I could look up and see Billy trying to reach inside the door to shoot me in the head. I watched the gun above my head as Billy kept pushing on the door. I was afraid Billy would just shoot through the door and kill me. I had to keep pushing on the door, while looking up at the gun, as Billy was trying to aim it toward my head.

The moment I dropped to the floor, I'd kicked over a big glass mirror which fell across my legs. It broke, cutting me. Now I was slipping on the broken glass and blood from my legs. I kept looking back at the door which led into the house. It was eight feet away from me. I knew if I let go of the door Billy would shoot me before getting to the other door. I kept pushing with everything I had, looking up at the gun the whole time as it was dangling there, searching for my head.

I was losing my grip on the garage floor; my bare feet were slipping from the broken glass and blood, the door started inching open. I kept pushing with all I had. I could still see the gun above me. Billy couldn't see where I was yet. I was getting tired of pushing. I said, "God help me please," as I lowered my head in defeat. I was going to let go of the door and take my chances.

Then I heard a shot from the gun which rang my ears. It was the same gunshot I heard weeks ago after the car fire! I thought Billy had shot me. The door closed, I reached up and locked the dead bolt. I started checking my head for blood as I ran back into the house. Looking out the kitchen window as I was running past it, I could see Billy making his way to the back door I had locked before going out to the garage to have a smoke. Billy kicked it open and stood in the doorway, looking down the hall to see where I was.

As I got to the bedroom, Tammy was standing up beside the bed next to the window with her arms crossed over her chest.

"What's going on?" She asked with fear in her eyes.

"Billy is here, "I yelled, "and he has a gun. He tried to shoot me in the garage."

I grabbed the gun from the night stand that Edward had given me to protect his daughter. I stood in the doorway of the bedroom where I could look down the hall to see where Billy was standing.

Lori started half way down the stairs, yelling, "What's going on?"

"Billy is here, go upstairs and call the police! Hurry, Lori," I shouted as I watched her turn around and run back up to her room.

Then bullets passed right by my face, hitting the closet door with the water heater in it. Water started leaking on Tammy's tile floor. I pointed the gun I had down the hall. I fired one shot to let Billy know I was armed too. I needed to keep Billy there until the police got here. I had six bullets in this gun. I had to use them wisely because the firing pin was bad, which made it almost impossible to reload.

I knew the doorway would be the safest place for me to stand, with all the wood nailed together to build a doorway. No bullet would come through it. That's why Billy was standing in the doorway of the kitchen.

I looked back at Tammy and told her to get out. All she had to do was open her window, push out the screen and step outside to run to get some help. We had discussed what to do if Billy ever showed up with a gun. Tammy did nothing; she wouldn't even call the police on her phone, which was lying next to her.

I stood in that doorway. Bullets were coming through the wall behind me going into the dresser I had brought over to Tammy's after I started staying there to protect Lori. Billy was firing a lot of bullets at me! He wasn't going to stop until I was dead. I was ok with that, as I felt pretty safe in the doorway as long as I had some bullets in my gun. I knew where Billy was and the police should be here any time. I fired another shot down the hall, letting Billy know I'm still here. "You haven't gotten me yet!"

I looked back at Tammy again. She was just standing in front of the window. I told Tammy to get out, but she just stood there, staring at me. I could see Tammy was saying goodbye to me with her eyes. I could see she was thinking, "Billy is going to kill you; he's a professional hunter and Billy is good with guns." Tammy was telling me goodbye, that's what I saw. She didn't have to say it, I saw it in her eyes. She was going to stand there and watch Billy shoot me and do nothing about it.

Billy started shooting two guns. Drywall and trim started flying in front of my face from the doorway of the bedroom I was standing in. I tucked myself tightly into the doorway, making myself as skinny as I could. When Billy stopped to reload his guns, I looked down the hall. I could see Billy standing out a little bit to see if he had hit me. I shot at Billy again. He jumped back behind the doorway to the kitchen.

I was down to three bullets left in my gun. I couldn't hear any sirens from the police, not even in the distance. "Where the hell are they?" I kept asking myself. Did Lori call the police like I told her to? They should be here by now, what's taking them so long?

Another round of gunfire from Billy, and I was still tucked tightly in the doorway of Tammy's bedroom. Tammy was still standing in front of the window, not moving, just staring at me. She wasn't talking, just staring, feeling sorry for me. I could feel her saying goodbye to me even when I wasn't looking at her. I turned towards Tammy, and I said, "Quietly, get out!"

Again, Tammy stood there. This time, I'd made up my mind. After my next two shots, leaving me with one bullet in the gun, if the police weren't here yet, I was going to leave out of the bathroom window like I planned the first day at Tammy's house. I had to save my life; I was not going to die here. Not now, not today, not trying to save Tammy, who didn't want to be saved.

Tammy was still in love with Billy, the man who was trying to kill me! I needed to get outside where I had better control of things, where I could think clearly. Once Billy stopped shooting to reload, I'd make my escape. I was done telling Tammy to get out; I needed to save my life now.

I fired two more shots toward Billy to let him know I was still there. As Billy was reloading his guns, I turned toward Tammy. I said, "It's time for me to go!" I turned real fast from the doorway, running into her bathroom, shutting the door behind me. I opened the window as far as it would open, about ten inches. I tried to jump out, but I feared hitting my head on the bottom frame.

My heart was pumping hard, and my adrenalin was also pumping. I needed to get out of Tammy's house. The opening was so narrow it knocked me back inside. I rubbed my head as I looked for the center of the opening, I jumped again, this time with the gun leading the way. I landed on Tammy's air conditioner and rolled off of it. I ran to the fence next door and jumped over the neighbor's privacy fence into Jerry's yard to get help. I knocked on Jerry's patio door several times, but he wouldn't answer his door. I took my last shot by his patio door, shooting my last bullet into the air hoping he'd hear it and open his door to help me.

Jerry didn't answer his door. Instead, he was hiding inside his house. I jumped the next fence into another yard knocking on their door, trying to get help. Once again, no answer. My heart was pumping fast. I just felt like Billy was behind me the whole time.

I walked around to the front yard, two houses down from Tammy's house. I kneeled behind a brick mailbox by the street looking back up at Tammy's house to see if Billy was out looking for me. Still, I couldn't hear any sirens in the distance.

A neighbor who was standing outside looking up my way. He saw the blood on my legs and saw I was carrying a gun hiding behind a mailbox. He ran back into his house scared. I started walking slowly back toward Tammy's house. Billy failed to get me like Devonna said. Now I was outside. I had control of things, even with an empty gun. Billy couldn't shoot me standing still, and he wouldn't get me on the move either.

Slowly walking up the sidewalk to get closer to Tammy's house, I heard four shots in a row coming from her house. I thought to myself, "Billy shot Tammy." I lowered my head. If Tammy would have only gotten out like I told her to, we'd be standing together right now. I walked up to the privacy fence where we hid one night. Then I climbed on top of the fence, sitting there watching the house, listening for more gunfire. Next, I saw three officers walking from the back of Tammy's house right past the window I had jumped out of. They were carrying shotguns and slowly made their way to the front of the house with their guns held up, ready for anything to happen. One of the officers yelled in the front door, telling Billy to put down his gun and come out with his hands in the air.

CHAPTER 36

The Police

"We know it's you, Billy Wolf. Now come out with your hands in the air," said the officer.

Then I heard two shots as the officer jumped to the corner of the house.

"I've been hit," an officer yelled as he jumped back into a corner to keep from getting shot again.

The other two officers started unloading their shotguns into the house, blowing a big hole in the front door as they were backing away from it down the driveway toward the street.

With joy in my voice and a smile on my face, I yelled at them to kill the asshole. I did my job. I knew it was over for Billy. He had no way out of this. Tammy couldn't help Billy this time. The officers looked back to where I was sitting on the fence to get a good view of everything going on.

One of the officers said, "Get out of here, you could get hurt."

I yelled back to them, smiling, "Billy already tried to shoot me, but he failed to get me. I'm Jim, the boyfriend." It was over for Billy this time.

By then another officer was parked down just two houses where I had been standing earlier by the mailbox. He yelled at me to come over to his car. I carried the gun in front of me so they could see it and not draw their guns on me. I already had enough guns pointed at me for the day.

The officer asked my name. "Jim Edwards," I said. "I'm Tammy's boyfriend. Billy surprised me this morning, holding a gun to my head at the garage door."

The officer asked, "Who is in the house with Billy?"

"Tammy and her daughter Lori Simmons," I said.

The officer asked, "Has anyone been shot?"

"Not while I was in there. I told Tammy to get out three times, but she just stood there. Lori, her daughter, is upstairs hiding in her closet. I jumped out that bathroom window over there when I ran out of bullets." I pointed at the open window in Tammy's bathroom.

The officer asked me if I would draw them a map of the inside of the house and put an L on where Lori was and put a T for Tammy. "So we know where they are inside the house. The swat team will need the map when they get here."

I drew a map of Tammy's house. I told him they could easily get Billy through the bathroom window. "That's where Tammy is; Billy will be in there with her."

The officer said they were waiting for a swat team. "They handle things like this all the time."

"Give me a gun," I said. "I'll stand by the bathroom window and shoot Billy's ass. I've repeatedly called you guys when Billy was stalking us. Billy even burned Tammy's car, but you didn't do anything about it because you didn't have blood or a body. Now you will probably have both."

"When I walked up the street," I said, "I heard four shots in a row. I figured Billy shot Tammy. That's why I was waiting across the street, to see if Billy would try and sneak out."

The officer said, "I'm sorry you went through this today. I understand having a gun to your head and running from someone shooting at you has ruined your day, but we will do everything we can to get Tammy and her daughter out of that house. I can see you are bleeding on your legs, did Billy get you with a bullet?"

"I don't think so," I said confused, "it happened in the garage when a glass mirror fell across my legs and broke. I was slipping on the floor from the glass and blood while trying to hold the door closed while Billy was trying to shoot me in the head through the gap in the door."

Then I saw Jerry, the next-door neighbor. He came running out of his house like a scared little girl, running down the street so he'd be safe. I wanted to ask him where he was hiding when I came to his door for help.

The officer said, "I'm going to take you down the street to a checkpoint we have set up. We will have the EMT's check you out and clean you up. That's where you will stay until it's over. Mr. Edwards, is there any way we can get into the garage? We need another way into the house. Is that your truck in the driveway? Do you have the keys with you?"

I said, "Yes, that is my truck in the driveway. The garage door opener is in my truck. My keys are in the house, so just break out a window to my truck and open the garage door. You have my permission."

The swat team arrived, a big brown swat truck with men coming out of it holding rifles, ready for action.

"I'm going to take you to the checkpoint now," said the officer.

"Look, I want to be here with Tammy," I said. "I don't want to leave her. I need to know if she is ok. I want to be here when she makes it out of there."

The officer said, "I will radio back to the checkpoint when I find out something on Tammy's condition. We need to get you cleaned up, Mr. Edwards."

CHAPTER 37

The Check Point

I got out of the police car and walked over to the check station. I was met by officers who took pictures of me, front and back. I stood there with my arms stretched out until they were done taking pictures and asking questions. As the police were taking a report from me, the EMT's were taking off my shirt to check me out and to see if I had been shot because of the blood stains. Then the EMT's started washing the blood off my legs and arms.

"I don't think so," I said. "I don't know," being in a confused state of mind. I wanted to cry because I was alive. I wanted to cry because Tammy was still in there with Billy. I just wanted to cry; all my emotions were scattered inside my head.

They could see I had been through a lot this morning. They knew I was still shaken up and scared at the same time. "I was so glad to be alive," was my first thought, and, "Nothing is better than being able to breathe another day." It was over for me, but Tammy was still in the house with Billy, unsure if she was dead or alive.

The officer asked me if I knew what kind of vehicle Billy was driving.

"Yes, I do," I said as I looked up past the officer. Down the street about a half a block sat Billy's black Avalanche with the paper tag still on it. "There's Billy's truck," I said as I pointed to it. It was parked on the wrong side of the road facing the wrong way on a dead-end street.

He sent officers down to look at the truck, and it was registered to a Billy Wolf.

I wondered where Billy was parking his truck while he was doing those things to us. A black truck at night without the lights on, couldn't be seen.

Then word came over his radio that Tammy had been shot, but she was still alive. They were trying to talk Billy into giving himself up. I was worried where Billy shot Tammy and how bad it was. Would she die without medical assistance soon, or was it not that serious? I could only wait for updates on her condition.

Kaelonnie, my sister who was at my birthday party the night before, came running up to me, crying as she hugged me tightly. Finally, someone who loved me was here. I wasn't alone anymore, surrounded by strangers. I was with my baby sister.

"I thought Billy shot you!" she said. I heard on the radio someone was being held hostage on Fredricksburg Street. If I hadn't come over last night, it wouldn't have ever dawned on me it was you. When I heard it, I called Tommy. I said, 'Jim is in trouble, get over to Tammy's house now! Tommy is on his way here.'"

The street was closed to traffic, as there were hundreds of people waiting to see the outcome. People who knew me were yelling my name to come over and asking me to give them details of what was going on. Lori Fullbright from Channel 6 news yelled my name, asking to give her a statement. Lori had covered my nephew's story after being shot from a stray bullet back in February.

I was worried Billy might be watching the news. He'd get mad if he'd seen me on the news talking about him. Maybe he'd shoot Tammy again, this time killing her. I waited at the checkpoint for more news on Tammy's condition.

My sister pointed out Billy's ex-wife and children that were standing behind me with smiles on their faces, like their dad was some kind of hero in all of this. I felt sorry for them. What Billy was doing wasn't something to celebrate. They were happy being part of this, their dad in the house barricaded holding Tammy hostage.

"Before you came here," she said, "I told Billy's family there better not be one scratch on my brother!" She told me they were bad people, not just Billy; the whole family. "Look at them," she said, "they are laughing and enjoying this."

Then I heard someone a familiar voice yelling my name.

Linda, Tammy's oldest daughter, came running up to me crying.

"What's going on?" she asked.

"Billy surprised me at the back garage door this morning," I said. "He held a gun to my head, but I was able to get away from him. I ran back into the house protect your mother, but she refused to leave like I told her to several times while Billy was shooting at me."

"How is Mom?" Linda asked.

"I don't know other than she has been shot," I said. "I don't know how bad her wound is, but they said she is still alive. That's good news."

Shortly after Linda came, the police brought Tammy's son Steven down to the waiting area.

Steven said Tammy had called him. She told him she had been shot. Billy told her she could call someone to say her goodbyes. Billy grabbed the phone. He said, "I shot your mom a little, she will be ok."

Her son was walking in circles making an ass of himself trying to call Billy on his cell phone. The police told him not to be calling Billy because they were trying to negotiate with him. But Steven would call Billy anyway. One officer told him if he called Billy one more time he'd be arrested for interfering with police business.

Steven started running his mouth, as usual; that's just who he was. Making a scene just to get attention from everyone.

An hour went by, and we heard they rescued Lori out of her bedroom. They brought Lori and Edward together to the checkpoint.

Tammy's family all gathered together and sat down on a curb waiting to hear some news. I walked over and sat down with them. Looking for a little comfort for what I had done for Tammy and Lori this morning. Maybe a hug, or a pat on the back. Thank-you, Jim would have been sufficient.

"Why did you leave my mom in there with Billy?" she asked, looking at me like I was the bad guy in all of this.

I told Lori I did the best I could do, "But your mom wouldn't leave like I told her to. She just stood there waiting for Billy."

I was in shock at what Lori just asked me. Hadn't I been through enough over the past five months? What more did this family want from me? What more could I have done? I went back into the house to save both girls from Billy. I had a gun fight with Billy, risking being shot. I could have opened the main garage door after locking the dead bolt and took off running down the street instead of going back inside to help the girls.

Ungrateful people, I thought to myself. I could see it in all of their eyes as I stood there looking at them. I was ready to go home at this point. I wanted to cry and scream out loud to each of them. Instead, I said nothing. I walked away, thinking to myself it wasn't three weeks ago when Lori threw a fit because Tammy wouldn't take her to a friend's house at 10:30 pm. Lori'd said, "I hope Billy shoots you!" Well, Lori got her wish today, but I was getting all the blame.

CHAPTER 38

The Hospital

Two hours later, we heard a loud boom which shook the neighborhood. Shortly after the police come over the radio and said they had Billy in custody. Tammy was being life-flighted to St. Francis Hospital.

My brother in law, Tommy, took me in his truck. Mine was still at Tammy's house. It seemed like it took forever to get there. I ran into the emergency room; it was full of people. I stood there and could see people talking softly with one another pointing over at me, saying, "He's the boyfriend." I didn't know any of them; I'd never seen them before. Who were they, and how did they get here so fast? I just stood alone in a corner against the wall, unsure if Tammy was even here yet.

"They rolled Tammy in on a gurney they took her to x-ray," Edward said. "Tammy was awake; the EMT's said her wound wasn't life threatening."

"That's good news," I said. "I'll just wait outside until Tammy is out of x-ray."

I waited outside sitting on a curb. The reality of what has happened today hadn't hit me yet. My mind was still cloudy and scattered. I didn't know if I was happy or sad. My girls showed up to the hospital. They came running up to me crying because they thought I'd been shot.

Paige, my youngest daughter, told me her mother went to my house banging on the door, trying to wake her up. She was worried Billy went there first and shot them.

Paige said, "Mom was crying when I opened the door. Mom just grabbed me hugging me. Mom told me that she heard you were being held hostage and someone has been shot over at Tammy's house."

My girls and I cried together during our long hug in the parking lot. Now the reality just hit me. My children almost lost their dad this morning. I had almost lost my children's smiles and laughter forever. I told my girls I loved them more than once. Maybe I didn't tell them enough before that morning, but they knew now! I had been through a lot.

My job was over; Billy was gone for good. I didn't have to watch my back anymore. Now I could sleep at night without having a gun close by.

I waited outside after my girls left in bare feet and bloody shorts for Tammy to get out of x-ray until she could have visitors. I needed to know why she didn't get out of the house. Maybe Tammy wouldn't want to see me after today. Her kids were blaming me for everything; would Tammy do the same? I needed to know how she felt after being shot.

Edward came outside; he asked me to come into the waiting room because the doctor wanted to talk to her close family. He told me "You are family to me, so I want you to be there. You're Tammy's boyfriend, now."

Again, Edward said I was Tammy's boyfriend "now." What did that mean?

The doctor came in and told us Tammy had been shot and she would be paralyzed from the waist down. He didn't know if she would ever regain feeling in her legs again. Tammy wanted to see her kids but only two at a time could go in.

After the doctor had left the room, Edward stood up. He said to his kids, "I have something to say to you kids about Jim. I want you all to thank him for going back into the house and doing what he did for Lori and your mom. This man has big balls. I don't see how he even walks. He did something I couldn't have done. I gave Jim a gun for protection, not a gun fight with Billy."

Wow, that felt good! Edward understood what I went through and what I did to protect the girls. Edward knew they were blaming me for Tammy getting shot.

The kids stood up, hugging me. They said, "Thank you, Jim, for everything."

Who cares if they meant it! I just needed to hear it.

The two oldest children, Linda and Steven, went in to see Tammy first. I guess they were in there for about twenty minutes. I was going to wait for Lori and Edward to visit before me. I wanted to be last in case Tammy and I were going to part ways. Maybe she was mad at me for leaving her alone with Billy. I doubt it, though; Tammy loved Billy, that's why she stayed.

Edward told me to go in with Lori; he'd wait. "Your Tammy's boyfriend now, I know you want to see her."

I'm Tammy's boyfriend "now?" Is that what Edward just said to me? I won the gun fight, so the winner gets Tammy, and the title of being the boyfriend?

"Thank you, Edward," I said. "I do have some questions that need answers. I need to know why Tammy stayed in the house with Billy. She stayed on her own. I told Tammy to jump out the window several times, Edward. But she just stood there looking at me."

I let Lori visit her mother while I stood out in the hallway; I wasn't sure if Tammy wanted to see me or not. I felt like she wanted to stay in there with Billy, and I needed to hear Tammy's excuse for not leaving. I waited for Lori to finish her visit before going in.

Lori came out shortly after her visit with Tammy.

"Jim, Mom wants to see you now," she said.

CHAPTER 39

The Master Bedroom

When I saw Tammy, laying there in bed as I walked in, my eyes started to water up. I was sad for her. We'd been through so much in the past five months, more than most couples go through in a lifetime. I needed to stay strong, to get my answers.

"I'm sorry, Tammy," I said, "I did my best trying to protect you and Lori."

Tammy was looking at me. "I'm the one who is sorry, Jim."

"For what?" I asked. I wanted to hear Tammy apologize for staying in the house with Billy. The truth would be revealed why she didn't get out.

"Billy cut up your jacket," she said. "He went into the closet looking for you after he shot me, and he came out with your jacket, pulled out his knife, and cut it up."

"I don't care about my jacket!" I said. "Why didn't you leave like I told you to three times? Why did you stay in there with Billy?"

"I don't know, I just froze!" she said.

I didn't believe it at all. Tammy was trying to protect Billy again, that's why she stayed in the house, staring at me, saying goodbye with her eyes. One day she will admit it, maybe not to me, but she'll tell the truth. Tammy thought Billy wouldn't hurt her if she stayed in there with him.

"Tammy, we went through the escape plan many times," I said. "I told you Billy would come through that door. I only had six bullets in the gun; when they were gone, I had to get out. I kept one bullet in the gun when I ran to the bathroom just in case I couldn't get out the window.

"I would have waited for Billy to kick in the door, then I would have used it. But I made it out. I jumped the fence to Mark's house to get help. But he wouldn't answer his door."

"When you ran into the closet, I threw you more bullets under the door," she said. "I thought you hid in the closet and needed more bullets."

"Tammy, you knew it would have taken me forever to reload that gun. The gun was so old, I didn't know if it would even shoot! Thank God it did. If I could have reloaded it, I would have stayed right where I was in the doorway shooting at Billy until the police came. Believe me; I could have just popped into the gun, I would have stayed there. But that's water under the bridge now. Billy is in jail, and you'll never see him again.

"Tammy, what happened when I left? How did Billy get to you?" I asked.

Tammy said, "Billy came scooting down the hallway floor on his butt. He pointed the gun at me, telling me to come out there where he was in the hallway. I just stood there. Billy got up and slowly walked into the bedroom looking for you, then he grabbed me, holding me tightly next him with his gun in my arm. Then Billy started yelling for you to come out of the closet. He said, 'I'm going to shoot Tammy if you don't come out.'

"Then Billy fired a bunch of rounds through your dresser mirror into the closet, thinking you were in there. You didn't come out, so Billy shot me in the arm. My legs just went out from under me at that point. I looked up at Billy and said, "You killed me!" Billy said I would be all right. That's when Billy went into the closet looking for you. He came out with your jacket. He took out his knife and cut it up. Billy was pissed you weren't in the closet."

Tammy went on, "Billy was mad you were gone. He said he wanted to kill you in front of me to show me how much he loved me. Billy held me up as a shield when the police started shooting at him in the bedroom. Then Billy took the mattress off your bed to hide us in the corner so they couldn't see us. Billy shot at the police through the bedroom window while they were trying to get Lori out.

"Billy shot his gun in the bedroom. I asked Billy, 'What are you shooting at?' Billy told me he shot the police do they sent in after him."

"I don't think the police would send a dog in after Billy," I said, "since he had guns."

"That's what Billy told me," she said. "He shot their police dog."

Tammy went on, "Billy took out a little baggy with some white powder in it. he snorted some of it, then he put some of it on my bullet hole, telling me it would help me with the pain. Then Billy put the gun under his chin like he was going to kill himself. But Billy chickened out, removing the gun. Billy did that a couple of times, but he never pulled the trigger.

"I think you beating Billy at his own game, something he had planned out for days in his mind, pissed him off. Now Billy was trapped with no way out of this, and he knew it. If Billy would have killed you like he planned, he would have given up to the police without shooting me—that's what Billy told me.

"I laid in that corner for what seemed like forever," she said. "Billy told me, 'This is it, Tammy, there's no way out of this. Either I kill myself, or give up to the police and go to prison for the rest of my life.' Then Billy put the gun under his chin again. I thought Billy would do it this time, but he didn't. Billy told me I could call one of my kids to say goodbye. Billy said if he couldn't have me, no one can.

"Billy told me he quit his job and took all of his money out of the bank. He took his grandkids to the fair Saturday night to spend one last day with them. Billy said he bought them four-wheelers on his credit cards to say goodbye to his grand-kids one last time. Billy took his birth certificate over to his ex-wife 's house. Sunday, Billy went to a friend's house asking for two guns, telling him he was going hunting. Billy said he was standing at the garage door since 4 am waiting for you to open it.

"Billy's plan was to kill you and take me away to his parent's land, hiding me. 'I have always loved you, Tammy,' was the last thing Billy said to me.

"The next thing I know, there was a loud boom, and the air was filled with some kind powder. I couldn't see my hand in front of my face. I heard yelling as the police came running in, tackling Billy on top of me. I was scared to death; I could-n't see what was going on around me, just yelling from the police saying they got Billy.

"The paramedics came in, put me on a stretcher and took me to the waiting helicopter."

"I'm sorry you went through that, Tammy," I said. "They threw in a flash bomb; I could hear it two blocks away. When I heard the loud boom, I knew they were coming in to get you. I'll never understand why you choose to stay in the house with Billy. I guess you have your reason."

Tammy's story of how Billy got to her made no sense at all. She was still standing in front of the bedroom window when Billy scooted down the hall on his butt. But she told me she went over to the bathroom door, throwing more bullets under the door, then running back over to the window until Billy showed up. It didn't make sense to me.

CHAPTER 40

ICU waiting room

The emergency room nurse came in. She told me they were getting ready to move Tammy to a room in ICU. It would be about an hour before I could see her again.

I told Tammy I needed to get some clean clothes and shoes. I was still walking around in bare feet with my bloody shorts on. Tammy's friend Penny come walking into the hospital as I was going out for a smoke. I told Penny they were moving Tammy to a room in ICU. I was trying to figure out how to get some clean clothes and shoes since everything was at Tammy's house.

Penny asked me what size shoe I wore. She'd run over to Walmart to get me a pair of flip flops until I could go back to the house to get some clothes. (Which would be in three days, the house was now property of the police until further notice).

Kaelonnie, my sister, asked me if I wanted her to get me some food before they went home. I asked Kaelonnie if she would pick me up some smokes and a twenty-dollar bill until I could get out of the hospital. "I'm not leaving Tammy's side right now," I told her.

Everyone was still inside the hospital talking to one another, trying to hear the real story of what took place this morning. Only I knew the real story. But I was just "The Boyfriend." I was ok with that. Not one person came up to me asking any questions about the shooting or how I was doing.

The shooting made the national news. It was October 1st, ironically the first day of Domestic Violence Month, and it was also my sister's birthday. I called her like I do every year. Since her birthday is the day after mine, it wasn't hard to remember it. She was so worried about me, and I wanted to break down and cry. But I held it in; I was still in a state of confusion. I told her as soon as Tammy was released from the hospital, we'd make a trip to Iowa to see her.

They moved Tammy to a room on the ICU unit. The waiting room was full of people waiting to see Tammy. I noticed Tammy's friend Lucy sitting alone. I walked over to say hello, give her an update on Tammy's condition, and tell her the story of what had happened.

Lucy turned to look at me, and with a loud angry tone in her voice said, "Why did you leave Tammy in that house?" She stared at me the whole time with the same black eyes Billy had that morning. She was mad at me. She would have shot me if she'd had a gun with her.

I looked around the room. I could see everyone looking at me. I turned and walked out of the waiting room feeling like I was a loser or maybe a coward, I don't know. I went back outside and sat on the curb, tears running down my cheeks, wondering if I did something wrong in saving myself. Was I supposed to stay in there and die for Tammy? Maybe I should have opened the garage door and took off running. This was the second person today who had blamed me for Tammy getting shot when in fact I tried saving Tammy from Billy.

I walked back up to the waiting room after having a smoke and gathering my thoughts. I had something to say, so I confronted Lucy. I wanted to say it loud enough for everyone in there to hear me.

With a loud tone in my voice, I said, "First of all, where were you people when Tammy told you what Billy was doing to her? Not one of you were there to lend a hand. You were only there to hear the story because none of you were brave enough to act on it. This has been going on long before I came into the picture. It's because none you cared enough, until now, because it's over.

"I'll tell you who her real friend is in all of this: it was me, the boyfriend. I didn't back down from Billy when he was stalking us and setting things on fire. I was the one at the door this morning, while Billy had a gun to my head. I was the one who ran back inside to save Tammy and Lori, while Billy was firing bullets at me! There were three lives I had to save from Billy this morning: Tammy, Lori, and mine. All three of us are living today, so I did my job.

"I told Tammy to get out of the house several times, but she chose to stay. Because she loves Billy and tried protecting him again. I wouldn't die for Tammy then, and won't die for her now! As for the rest of you, who think I'm a coward for saving my life today," I looked at Lucy as I said, "Everyone can kiss my ass!"

I walked outside to have a smoke again. I really needed to think things over from this point. Should I just get my things and leave Tammy as soon as the police opened up the house and let Tammy's so-called friends take care of her now? Not once did I hear anything bad about Billy; their fingers were pointed to me.

177

Kaelonnie brought me some smokes and the twenty dollars I asked for. She could see I was upset. Kaelonnie asked, "What's wrong Jim?"

I told Kaelonnie what people were saying about me jumping out of the window to save myself, leaving Tammy in the house with Billy.

"None of those people have a right to say anything," she said. "You did more than any man would have, so don't feel bad. And neither Tammy's kids nor her friends have a right to say anything about what you did. Billy was there to kill you, Jim, and if those people have a problem with it, they can come to me."

I went back inside after talking with my sister. I felt better after what she had said to me. Tammy's mother, Mary, came walking up to me.

Mary asked if I would tell her the real story, not the one going around the waiting room.

"Mary, I'd love to tell her the story as soon as I check on Tammy's condition," I said.

Then Lucy walked up to me, with a different look on her face. "I apologize, Jim, for what I said. Tammy is my best friend; that's why I was mad. You left her in the house with Billy."

"Lucy," I said with a firm voice, "back off!" Then I walked away. I had nothing to say to her. Lucy had shown me her true colors earlier.

I never left Tammy's side while she was in ICU except for a smoke or something to eat or to visit the chapel to pray for Tammy's recovery.

CHAPTER 41

Tammy's ICU Room

I entered the chapel to talk with the Lord. I walked up front and dropped to my knees with tears running down my cheeks, barely able to speak. I knew the Lord had just saved me from being killed earlier today, but I had another favor to ask of him.

"Lord, I ask you, please heal Tammy's legs. Forgive Tammy for her sins of the past. I ask you Lord with all my heart, give me the healing hands so I may heal Tammy. Lord, I pray to you now, with all my heart and soul, please let Tammy walk again."

I raised my head and looked at Jesus on the Crucifix, hanging in front of me.

I said, "Thank you, Lord, for sparing my life today. Thank you, Lord, for sending me help holding the door closed from Billy. Forgive me, Lord, for thinking I could do this alone, without asking you for help sooner. Lord, I'm putting this in your hands. I know you will do the right thing. Amen."

I sat in a pew for about an hour after my prayer, crying because I needed to. I was trying to sort things out. Maybe I was waiting for an answer from God. I was still in shock from everything which happened this morning. Talking with God was just what I needed to clear my mind.

I returned to Tammy's room after my prayers to the Lord. I was tired and needed to get some rest. I'd been on my feet since 7:23 this morning. I was ready to drop, and I needed some sleep soon.

That first night at the hospital was the most painful night I have had in years. I was supposed to get a root canal done after finishing the Keller Williams job. I was in pain; my tooth was killing me, almost bringing tears to my eyes. I really needed painkillers, and Tammy's nurse wouldn't give me anything for the pain. She told me I'd need to go to the emergency room if I wanted anything for my toothache, but I wasn't leaving Tammy's side. I needed penicillin to kill the infection and something to stop the pain.

I called my daughter, Paige, hoping she would have some penicillin around her house I could take to relieve the pain I was in. She told me she had about fifteen capsules left and brought them to the hospital.

I slept on the foldout chair every night, sometimes with my head laying on Tammy's legs. I did the same thing with my mother while she was dying of breast cancer.

Every time I closed my eyes, I'd see Billy standing there with the gun to my head, staring at me with those lifeless black eyes. I'd jerk my head up, opening my eyes to see if Billy was standing there in front of me again. I knew this was going to haunt me for some time to come. I was getting less sleep now than I was watching out for Billy!

Tammy slept for the first couple of days, waking up for an hour or two each day. I couldn't wait for her to wake up so I could hear more of her story of what went on while she was with Billy in the bedroom. Tammy woke up for about an hour one day, and she said Billy told her he killed her cat, Jack, the night he cut the wiring in my Jeep. Then she starting mumbling stuff that didn't make any sense at all. I knew the drugs were working. I told Tammy to get some rest and that I'd be right here when she woke up.

I thought Billy being in jail would put an end to the drama and turmoil in our lives, but Lucy went in to visit Tammy while I was on break getting some fresh air. Lucy told Tammy about what she said to me, and what I said back to her when she tried to apologize to me. Of course, Lucy didn't tell the whole story of how she had acted towards me in the waiting room.

"Jim, you should forgive Lucy," Tammy said, "because we are best friends."

"Let me tell you how it is, Tammy," I said, "you don't just yell out hurtful things to people like Lucy did to me, assuming I'd forgive her. Lucy has to figure out she was a dumbass for saying what she did to me and saying it loudly with everyone looking at me. Lucy thinks she can just apologize to me and that's it, we are the best of friends now. It's not going to happen, Tammy. Maybe later, who knows. Why am I the blame for all of this, Tammy, when it was Billy who shot you?"

I saw Lucy in the hall and had a few choice words for her. "Lucy, you are Tammy's friend, not mine. I've met you only once since dating Tammy. Not once were you ever around when things were happening to us, nor did you offer any help. Right now, I don't accept your apology! Will I ever accept it? I don't know; it's not on the top of my list at this time."

It felt good to say those words to her, just something else off my chest. I don't offer respect to anyone; they have to earn it if they want it from me. I don't care who visits Tammy; just keep me out of their conversations from now on.

CHAPTER 42

Going back to the House

I was told I could return to the house October 4th, as the police had completed their investigation. I pulled into the driveway that morning about 10 am and sat there in my truck, looking at the house. I was not sure if I wanted to go in.

I was scared...what if someone was in there hiding? Billy's brother, maybe, or some other family member waiting to get me? I looked at all the windows carefully for any kind of movement. Most were shot out and covered with plywood. I knew it would be dark and creepy inside, with bullet holes in every wall.

I wanted to leave without going in because everything started playing back in my head. I put the truck in reverse, but I held down the brake, I had to face my fears. I hit the garage door opener and watched the door slowly open, getting ready to push on the gas if I saw anyone coming out of the garage. The door opened, and I saw my Jeep was still sitting in there. I looked at the garage door in the back where I faced Billy just a few days ago. I needed to find answers; what Billy shot at when the door shut.

I put my truck in park and left it running as I got out really slowly, making my way to the garage. The door which leads into the house was open. I could see into the kitchen, the door Billy had kicked open that fateful morning, and I could see my birthday cake still on the table, untouched, with balloons still hanging in the air.

I took a deep breath, taking one step inside. I stopped to listen for any movement, then took another step further. I could see my security monitor was still on, showing my truck in the driveway.

The house looked like a battle zone. It was dark, the furniture flipped over with the covers ripped off, and holes filled every wall. The police cut big circles with a saw to get bullet holes as evidence to be used against Billy in court.

The police told me they couldn't find bullets anywhere around the garage door I said Billy fired at me. I had to look myself to prove them wrong. Billy shot his gun really close to my head; it rang my ears. I knew if I walked through the whole event, I could see in my mind what happened to the bullet Billy fired that morning.

I walked around out back to the side of the house where Billy was standing at the door. Down on the sidewalk by the door was a dime waiting for me. I knew my mother was there with me that morning. I looked hard everywhere but couldn't find a bullet hole anywhere. But then I spotted drops of blood in the grass.

If Tammy's Boxer, Roxie, came around to get Billy, then Billy would have pulled the gun out of the doorway, shooting the dog. Roxie would have gone into the shed which sat in a corner of the back yard. I walked into the shed, then to the back of the shed in a corner. I found a big puddle of dried blood on the floor. I followed the dripping blood into the kitchen, little drops on the tile leading toward Tammy's bedroom. Roxie went into the bedroom to say goodbye to Tammy. Billy shot Tammy again, telling her it was a police dog sent in after him.

Now it made sense! When I said, "God help me, then lowering my head in defeat, God sent Roxie around to save me from Billy. That's why the police couldn't find a bullet; it was inside the dog!

Down the hall where I was standing in the doorway to Tammy's bedroom hiding from Billy's gun fire, it looked like someone used a machine gun on the closet door with the water heater.

I hurried back outside. Being in the house again felt so creepy. I walked out to the back yard to calm my fears. Outside, I was still in control, I felt safe! I could see the broken window in the master bedroom where Billy was shooting at the police while they were trying to get Lori out.

This was going to take me a long time to fix. I would have to bring my trailer with all my tools and have a dumpster delivered to put all the shot-up furniture in. I needed to face my fears and find the strength and courage to walk inside Tammy's house to start working on it. This was not going to be easy for me to do.

I'd have to be here every day at 8:00 am working until just before dark. I'm wasn't quite ready to be here after dark yet. Not alone, anyway.

Tammy's insurance adjuster wanted to come to the house to total up the damage so I could start the repairs to Tammy's badly shot up house. Tammy had talked to the insurance adjuster early that morning. He wanted to see the divorce papers showing Tammy was divorced from Edward; that way the check for the damages would be made out to Tammy alone.

CHAPTER 43

Linda's Mind Games

Linda said she would meet the adjuster at the house. I needed to be there, too, because it was my bedroom suite Billy shot up in anger towards me when I was not there for him to kill. I also had some of my artwork hanging on her walls in the living room with bullet holes in them, so I needed to be there to claim my losses, too.

The insurance adjuster met us there around 10 am, October 5th to access the damages. After walking through the house for about an hour, his final estimate totaled $12,000.00. He told me my stuff was included in the estimate, and I would have to collect my part from Tammy, since my things were in her house.

I was ok with him adding my things in the estimate. I knew Tammy wouldn't stiff me on repaying me. Now I could start working on the house. I had plans to make it different than it was before the shooting to help erase everything that has happened the morning of October 1st.

The insurance adjuster asked me to get the divorce papers so he could make the check out to Tammy Simmons.

Linda asked, "Why do you need the divorce papers?"

The insurance adjuster answered, "I need them so I can make the check out to Tammy Simmons. Otherwise, I have to put both Tammy and Edward's name on the check."

"I'll go upstairs to get the divorce papers," I said. "Tammy told me where they were."

Linda said, "Bullshit, you can make the check out to my Dad and Mom!" Then she called Tammy at the hospital. Linda said, "I'm having the check made out to you and Dad."

Here we go again! Linda was running things her way, or she would throw a childish fit for not getting her way. "Why am I still here?" I kept asking myself. I'm going to have to deal with Linda's mind games and power struggles she has with her mother.

Linda wasn't done yet. Later, while up at the hospital talking to her mother, Linda said, "Mom, I have some friends who are going to give you a bid for the work to be done on the house." Linda knew this is what I did for a living at the time.

Linda said, "Mom, they are cheap, and they do good work too."

Tammy looked at me; I was just waiting for her decision. If she chooses Linda's friend's, I was going to pack my things and move back to my house. Then Tammy looked back at Linda and said, "Jim will take care of it."

"Bam!" I thought to myself. "Take that you back-stabbing spoiled little brat!" I looked at Linda's face, turning from all smiles to the serious look of, How did that happen?

Linda said, "Well, let them at least give you a bid, Mom."

One last try from Linda. She wasn't going to leave without trying to get her way one last time.

Tammy looked at her again and said, "Jim will take care of it. Thank you, sweetheart."

Tammy looked over at me. She asked, "You will take care of it. Right?"

"I'll start first thing tomorrow morning," I said. "Cleaning the house and moving everything into the garage. I'll take my Jeep back to my house so I'll have room for everything.

Linda was not happy when she left the hospital room. Somehow, I was able to steal her power for one brief moment. I was sure she'd be back. I bet the wheels of "How to beat Jim" inside her head were turning even faster now.

I hadn't the slightest clue why Linda disliked me so much. She'd been like this from day one. I've never said anything out of context to her. I've always ignored her rudeness towards me, thinking one day she'd realize I was good for her mother. I'd rather Linda just come out and say what she was thinking instead of playing her game with me. I just finished a five-month game with Billy and Tammy. I wanted to tell Linda, "No more games, I'm done, game over."

CHAPTER 44

Repairing Tammy's house

Saturday morning, I left the hospital at 7 am sharp. I asked my brother-in-law, Tommy, to meet me over at the house to help me move some things out into the garage. Besides, I needed someone there for a peace of mind to help me lose my fear of being back at the house alone.

We started moving things out into the garage, stacking the best we could, to make room for everything. In the master bedroom, we started taking apart the bed. It was full of bullet holes from Billy's anger of not getting me. I can't imagine what was going through Billy's mind when I wasn't in the house.

The mirror on my dresser Billy had shot through thinking I was in the closet was shattered, laying all over the top of my dresser. My clothes in the dresser were full of shotgun pellets from the police. I had just remodeled Tammy's bedroom three weeks ago, putting in new a floor, painting the walls, and bringing my bedroom suite over. Now I would have to do it all over again.

Tommy and I started pulling up the floor after moving things out of the bedroom. I came across a little square baggy sticking halfway under the baseboard trim in the corner where Tammy and Billy were barricaded from the police. I left it there and called the police to check it out.

The policeman pulled it out with his tweezers and tested it. "Yes," he said, "it's cocaine." He made out a report and told me if I find anything else to call them.

That first day we had everything stacked in the garage. Now I had enough room to start working hard repairing the house. Tommy said he would pick up some drywall before coming back the next day so that we could repair the little holes. I started taking doorways apart to widen them for Tammy's wheelchair to fit through.

At this time I wasn't sure how long Tammy was going to be in the hospital, but I knew if I worked every day for a couple of weeks, I could have it close to being finished by the time she was released. Besides, during the week, I would be alone working on the house, which haunted my mind all weekend.

Tammy was moved out from ICU to a room on the ninth floor. They came in twice a day, sitting Tammy up and working her legs. I watched closely because I would have to do it when she returned home.

Monday morning back at the house. I pulled into the driveway, and again I kept my truck in reverse as I opened the garage door, watching it closely. I wasn't ready to let my guard down just yet and assume everything was ok. I did the same thing every morning for about a week.

I decided to walk around the house, count the broken windows, and call the glass company to come out to replace the broken glass. Walking around the house, I was able to look inside to make sure nothing was moved or moving.

The glass company came out around 10 am to start replacing the broken glass. I was able to enter the house feeling better about not being alone while they were there. Fear is one spooky thing when it invades your mind.

I wanted to fix all the doors and windows that were broken so I could lock up the house every night before leaving. The front door still had plywood over it, along with the one side window next to the front door. I spent all day replacing the front door. I ordered half an inch tempered plate glass for the side window that hung beside the front door. I wanted to frame the plate glass in for safety reasons.

It was only the things Tammy told me about Billy's family that kept me spooked while working on her house. She had told me the whole family was rotten to the core. Billy's brother, Mike, always did the fighting for Billy. He would pull out his knife and cut people. I wasn't too worried about someone coming after me with a knife as long as I could see them coming. So with any little noise I heard, I stopped working, looked in all directions, then continuing my work. Sometimes I had to go outside for a bit take in some deep breaths. It felt like I was holding my breath under water, and I had to come up for a breath every now and then.

While I was working long days alone, one day the neighbor lady across the street brought me some lunch. We stood in the driveway and talked about everything that had gone on over the past five months after meeting Tammy. She had told me because of what I did for Tammy, the neighborhood would be back to normal. With Billy being gone, she could let her kids play outside again. "My children were afraid of Billy. I kept them in the house while he was around. I didn't trust that man."

At last! Someone appreciated what I did; not once did she blame me for leaving Tammy in the house with Billy. She was just happy Billy was gone for good.

She said, "I believe Tammy stayed in the house because she still loved Billy. Those two always fought, and they always had the police involved in their fights. But they'd always get back together."

"That was my thought too," I said. "I'm sure Tammy thought Billy wouldn't hurt her if she stayed in there with him. If Tammy knew her life was in danger, fearing that Billy would hurt her, she would have escaped out the window like I told her to."

I thanked her for the bowl of soup and handed the bowl back. She gave me a hug before going back to her house across the street. Tammy had some really great neighbors. Too bad she didn't take the time to get to know them.

I was making headway on the house. Into my second week, most of the holes were covered up. I started some painting in the master bedroom. Soon I would be painting the living room. I was giving the house a new clean paint smell. No more nasty pet odors filled the air. For the first time, I felt safe inside the house; all the windows fixed, new steel doors front and back, and wrought iron screen doors, all with deadbolts on them for safety.

I spent the nights at the hospital with Tammy, showering and sleeping in the fold out chair. The nurses would come into Tammy's room every three hours to turn her over, which woke me up. I wasn't getting a full night's sleep, but I was getting more than I was while on watch for Billy.

Linda would return for more complaining about something I was doing, or not doing, to her liking. This time her complaint was I hadn't given her a key to the house since I'd changed the doors and locks to the house. Linda was reaching for any kind of control, even if it's as petty as keys to the house.

Tammy mentioned Linda's complaint to me when I arrived that night from working on the house. Tammy asked me if I would give Linda a key to the house.

"Why does Linda want a key to the house, Tammy? Your children have only been over once since I started working on the house. They told me they'd finish painting the kitchen for me one night and it would be done when I returned the next morning.

"But in the morning, there was a bigger mess for me to clean up then what the police left! My brushes were left in the paint pans, overnight with paint still in the pan. Pizza boxes were left in the living room on the floor. The patio was full of empty beer bottles, like they had a party after I left. Besides, all my tools are laying inside the house. I would feel better if I was the only one with a key right now. Surely you can understand that."

Tammy said, "I do understand, thank you for explaining it to me. I'll tell Linda, if they want to see the house or help with anything, to go over when you are there."

I couldn't seem to get a break! My labor was free of charge. I was fronting Tammy the money for the materials until she gets her check from the insurance company to pay me back.

I hadn't had any calls for my business to bid on any work since Keller Williams. I'm starting to worry; Tammy's house will cost me around $6,000.00 out of my pocket to finish. I needed to call Devonna again, asking her what's going on with my business, and why I haven't had any calls for work.

I called Devonna after locking up the house for the night. I sat in my truck in Tammy's driveway to hear the news Devonna had for me.

"Devonna, how are you, pretty lady?" I asked.

"I'm fine, dear," she said. "How are you? I heard on the news and read about in the paper about what Billy did. How is Tammy doing?"

"That's why I'm calling you, Devonna. The doctor said she would never walk again. Can you look at the cards for me and tell me what's going on?"

"Yes, let me shuffle them," she said.

I could hear Devonna shuffling the cards, laying them down with a snap from each card. Then there was silence as Devonna was looking at the message from each card.

"Jim, you should be dead," she said. "That man was there to kill you. I can see a lot of bullets flying around you that day."

"I know, bullets were coming all around me," I said. "Billy had two guns, and he used both of them."

"Jim, did you know Arch Penny Michael was swatting bullets away from you that morning?" she said. "This was terrible what you went through, and I can see everything Billy did to try and get you."

"You told me on my last reading Billy would fail to get me," I said, "and you were right! Now Billy's in jail like you said he would be. But Tammy has the legs you were talking about, not treading water. Do the cards show if she will ever walk again?"

"It doesn't look like Tammy will ever walk again," she said. The doctor was right.

"This is going to be hard on me," I said, "Tammy not being able to walk."

"Jim, I see you leaving Tammy after three attempts. After the third attempt, you leave for good."

"Oh, no, I couldn't leave Tammy!" I exclaimed. "God would be mad at me if I left her, Devonna."

"Jim, you'll be all right. Right now, the angels have stopped all of your work coming in until you finish Tammy's house. Then you will leave. I'm sorry it's not what you wanted to hear, but right now, that's what the cards are telling me will happen down the road."

"Thank you for the reading, Devonna. I love you very much. You've helped me so much through all of this."

"I love you too, Jim," she said. "Now take care."

How could Devonna be wrong? Maybe the angels were stopping my business calls for now. I hadn't had any calls since the shooting; besides I wouldn't have time to do my own work and finish on Tammy's house. I could understand that happening.

The house was coming together quite nicely. Neighbors stopped by often to take a look at what I had done up to this point. In the wall which divided the dark computer room and kitchen, I cut a big hole, installing a counter top with bar stools for a place to chat while Tammy was on her computer. Plus, it gave the room more light. It was always so dark in the far corner of her house.

I then cut a half circular hole in the wall between the kitchen and the living room, giving it more light. Now you could see in the kitchen when Tammy was in there, in case she fell out of her wheelchair. I wanted to open up her house on the inside so you could talk without yelling around walls. It wasn't so dark inside Tammy's house anymore during the daytime.

Tammy was being moved to the fourth floor. She'd have therapy from 8:30 to 12:00 noon. Tammy would be in a class to teach her how to cook things living out of a wheelchair. She needed that because I had to work, and Tammy would have to take care of herself until I returned. The hospital told me her return home date was November 17th. They'd send someone to the house to check out my work to make sure it was handicap accessible. I'd done everything on the list they'd given me before starting the repairs to Tammy's house. I was ready for their inspection.

The house was perfect inside. Mint green covered the kitchen walls. It looked great with black wrought iron candle holders with dark cabinets surrounding the walls.

The master bedroom was painted olive green, perfect color for my dark cherry sleigh bed. I hung my four-foot Penny picture at the foot of the bed. It was the first thing you saw after waking up. I had filled in the bullet holes to my bed and stained it back to color. I also replaced the mirror which was shot out. The bedroom was perfect, with no signs a shooting ever took place.

The living room was painted with a light brown paint. Tammy had no furniture left, except an entertainment center, which was old. It was a light oak color, ugly but sturdy. I took it apart and painted it flat black. You couldn't tell it was the same old entertainment center. I decided to bring my furniture over to Tammy's house, since I'd be living there caring for her every day from now on.

Word had gotten around about how hard I was working on the house. A couple of Lori's friends' mothers stopped by to look at the house to see what I had done to it. They just love it and offered to do the final cleaning: laundry, dishes, mopping floors, etc. I told them the date Tammy was to return home. I wanted to get my furniture moved over before she returned. Every day they'd come over, spending the whole day cleaning until it was time for their daughters to be picked up from school. They were such a blessing to me! When they finished cleaning one room, I'd fill it with furniture and pictures from my house.

Back at the hospital, Tammy was going to her classes during the day. She was excited about going and learning new things. I think she just liked the attention she was getting. But, as you know, good news is always followed by bad news with Tammy's children.

"Linda was upset you painted that entertainment stand," Tammy said.

Linda told Tammy her dad bought that for her and they assembled it together. But I knew it was all about getting me in trouble with Tammy.

"Jim, could you just apologize to Linda for painting it?" she asked.

Linda was back using her psychological tactics to manipulate her mother into taking her side on things. Telling Tammy it had sentimental memories was Linda's way of manipulating Tammy. All I'd heard from Linda about her dad, Edward, was how much he bitched about everything. Linda had never had anything good to say about her father since I met her, In fact, Linda hasn't said anything nice about anyone since I met her. Linda has learned well from Billy; always having a sour look on her face and never liking anyone.

I looked at Tammy and said. "You're kidding me, right? I work on your house every day until dark. Then I come up here with you, sleeping in a chair while doing my best to have everything done before you are released from the hospital, and Linda comes up here when I'm at your house working to talk behind my back? She's starting her crap again, all because I painted a stand? I could have thrown the stand in the dumpster with the rest of your broken furniture, but I kept it. I painted it so it would match what I was doing to your house. Tammy, I'm really getting frustrated with the bullshit your daughter and your friends are saying about me behind my back,"

"Who is saying things behind your back?" she asked.

"Linda has bitched three times now, Tammy: the insurance check, the keys to the house, and now the entertainment stand. I'm sure Linda's not done yet. Give her some more time to think of something else."

"I'm sorry, Jim," she said. "I let Linda run things when Edward left me. I wasn't in any shape to take care of things, so Linda did it for me."

"Tammy, I can run my own things and my own life. I'm forty-seven years old. I don't need some kid running my life for me. But if Linda wants to run things for you, then she can finish the house. I'm tired of people interfering with the way I'm doing things. I always talk to you before making any decision, right?"

"Yes, you do, Jim," she said.

"Then tell your friends and family to back off let me finish the house. I 'm using my money to work on your house until you pay me back. So I'll do things my way on the inside until finished."

Tammy had one week left before returning home. The two mothers and I worked very hard cleaning the house to a spit shine. I moved all my furniture into Tammy's house. My big couch and chair went perfectly in the living room. I covered her walls with the paintings I had in my home. My house sat empty, and I wasn't sure if I'd be able to make any payments on it. I was hoping Tammy would get her check soon so I could make my house payment and my pay bills, which were due. Even if my house were empty, I could buy furniture to fill it again.

CHAPTER 45

Making Love

On Sunday while sitting in the hospital room with Tammy being bored, I asked her if she would like to take a drive over to see the house. I was ready for her to see it. That way we could be alone for a while.

"Do you think we can leave?" she asked.

I talked to the nurse and got a four-hour pass. I helped Tammy into my truck. I was taking Tammy back home for the first time since the shooting. On our way, Tammy's phone rang.

Linda was asking Tammy, "What we were doing to today?"

Tammy told Linda we were on our way to the house. "Jim got a four-hour pass for me, so Jim is going to show me the house! I'm so excited to see it!"

Linda was pissed again! "I wanted to be there when you saw the house, Mom. I'm at work, I don't get off for another two hours."

Tammy said, "It's ok honey, you'll be here when I come home for good next week. Besides, Linda, Jim and I wanted to be alone for a while."

I wanted the phone from Tammy to tell Linda to get a life to leave us alone. But Tammy wouldn't give me her phone. She kept swatting at my hand.

"Things were going to be different from now on," I told to myself. "I'm tired of turning the other cheek and kissing her children's butts. From now on I'll stand up for myself. I'll not take any more abuse from her kids or her friend Lucy."

Tammy loved the house. She had tears in her eyes when I wheeled her in through the front door.

"Oh, Jim, it's perfect. Isn't that your furniture?" she asked, "It's beautiful, what you've done to my house."

"I had to bring my furniture to your house because yours was shot up. Everything you had was stacked into one big pile here in the living room Anything broken I threw it in the dumpster."

Tammy wanted to see the bedroom. She wheeled herself over to the doorway. She was amazed!

"I love the Penny picture hanging on the wall," she said. "Help me lay on the bed please; I need to get out of this chair."

I lifted Tammy out of her chair and placed her in the middle of the bed.

"Lay on the bed with me, Jim; it is so comfortable. I remember how good I slept in your bed when we met," she said.

"Tammy, if I lay down on my bed, I won't get up for hours," I said.

"Jim, I want to have sex with you right now."

I wasn't ready for that! I'm not sure I could. Besides, she couldn't feel it anyway. Finally, an awkward moment in our relationship. How was I going to talk myself out of this?

"I can't feel it down there anymore, but I can feel it inside my heart, I need you to make love to me, Jim."

After it was over, I realized I never wanted to do that again! I wasn't comfortable with it. I didn't enjoy it at all. How would I tell Tammy the next time I wanted to sit this one out? I knew this was going to be a hard topic to talk about with her. And when that time came up again, I would handle it. Right now Tammy was happy, and that's all that mattered.

Tammy's kids showed up an hour before we left to go back to the hospital. Linda had that sour look on her face again, as usual, because Tammy had seen the house without Linda's blessings or permission. Linda hated me. For what reason, only she knew. She wasn't on top of my friend's list either.

"Why did you bring my mom home in your truck?" Linda asked.

"Because we had no place to put her wheelchair on my motorcycle," I said.

I waited silently for Linda to open up her mouth again, but this time I was going to let her have it. Instead, she faked being happy for Tammy's sake. Giving me the "Wolf Look" from time to time. It wasn't fair; I was always on pins and needles when Linda came around.

When we arrived back at the hospital, the nurse asked how the trip went. Tammy was all smiles. She missed her home but knew in a week she would be back there for good.

"Tammy, after all of this is over and we are back at your house, I'd like for us to take a trip to Iowa to see my sister," I said, "because we need a getaway for a while. My family hasn't seen me since all of this has happened."

Tammy said, "Ok! That will be fun. I like your sister, Jim."

That last week flew by. Tomorrow Tammy gets to return home. Little does she know, the house will be full of people waiting for us to pull into the driveway. She'll be so surprised to see everyone waiting outside to greet her back home.

Tammy's family from Iowa was going to be there. Her mother who gave her up for adoption, along with her brothers and sisters, would also be there. Some of Tammy's friends I haven't met would be coming to her welcome-home party.

I was nervous, being the boyfriend, how they'd act toward me. Everyone else had blamed me for saving my life; would they do the same?

CHAPTER 46

Returning Home

There were welcome home signs in her yard with balloons floating as we pulled into the driveway. Tammy was all smiles. Why wouldn't she be? Her life was going to different now; Billy wasn't running the show. Now her friends could come and visit her anytime they wanted to. I wheeled Tammy into the house where she was greeted by her family from Iowa and friends who were too afraid to come over when Billy was with her. I just stood back in a corner and watched Tammy receive hugs from everyone who loved her. Tammy loves being the center attention, and she was getting plenty of it. No one said anything to me—no greeting of any kind, no thank you's, no hugs. They just pushed Tammy into the kitchen so they could hear her side of the story.

Edward was there, and he pulled me off to the side.

"Jim, you did a beautiful job on the house," he said. "You have talent! I couldn't believe that was the entertainment stand I bought for Linda until she told me what you did to it."

"Yeah, I almost took an ass chewing over that stand," I said. "Linda was mad at me for painting it.

"Thank you, Edward," I told him. "I just wanted things to be perfect when Tammy came home. I'm going to step outside to have a smoke, and let Tammy have her moment with everyone."

I sat out on the patio for a bit, smoking and listening to the laughter going on inside the house. Not one person thanked me for what I had done for standing up to Billy. I felt alone in all of this, after everything I did for Tammy. There was no thanks waiting for me, "The Boyfriend."

The five months of hell were over—no more fires, no more guns. Of course, our lives had changed a lot now that Tammy can no longer walk. I'd have to be the legs for two people now. I wondered what was going to happen. I could still feel the tension from Tammy's children. I know they don't like me; that was going to make my life hard, being here. I took the lawnmower out of the shed and started cutting the grass out front while everyone inside listening to Tammy's story.

Everyone packed up their hugs and kisses, going home around 9 pm. Once again it was dark outside. Even though the house was locked up good, I was still gun shy about sleeping there. I could still see Billy's eyes when I closed mine.

Tammy and I sat in the living room. We talked about the things I did to the house while she was in the hospital. I told her I had some trim work which needed finishing in the master bathroom before I could start upstairs.

I mentioned to Tammy I had spent $6,000.00 on her house for materials. I needed to make my house payment, along with bills as soon she could pay me back. "I have all the receipts if you'd like to see them. I'd like to put that money back into my bank account as soon as I can. My bills are past due, Tammy. I'm going to lose my house if I don't catch up on my payments soon."

"As soon as I get my Insurance check, I'll give you your money back, Jim," she said. "Besides this is our house now. We're a couple, right?"

"Yeah, we're a couple, Tammy, but I'd like to put that money back into my account, or I'll lose my house if I don't make some payments soon."

"You can rent it out," Tammy said, "while you are living here. Now we'll have two houses, and later we can buy more after we pay your house off. That's what couples do, right?"

"You're not getting the point, Tammy. That was my money earned before you came along. I'd like it back in my account when you get your check. Then what money is made while we are together will be our money, as a couple."

Tammy was giving me the run around about paying me back. What has happened during these five months was a game to Tammy. It wasn't a game to me. I lost either way. I lost my life without being shot. My beautiful home and all my things which filled the inside of my home were now at Tammy's house. I felt sorry for her. She had nothing left after the shooting, while my house sat empty across town. How did this happen, I wondered, how did I lose my things?

For the next couple weeks, things were very hard for me taking care of Tammy. I was her caretaker and her house cleaner. Every morning after getting up, I let the dogs outside. I picked up their pee pads off the floor they failed to use during the night. I had to mop the kitchen floor. I'd start a load of bed pads because Tammy would use five pads per day, sometimes more. Start some coffee, and while it was brewing, I'd step out to the garage have a smoke like I did that fateful morning. Then I'd go back into the bedroom to cath Tammy, keeping her dry. I did that every two hours during the day until I had some clean bed pads to put under her. I found myself being Tammy's nurse, doing things only someone in the medical field would do.

What had happened to me? Where did my life go? I found myself trapped in her house all over again. I hadn't taken the time to look at the beauty of God's creation. I hadn't looked at the sky, moon, or the stars in months. I hadn't seen my children since the day of the shooting or my grandkids since meeting Tammy back in May. Tammy was taking my life away from me again, even after Billy was gone, only because I was manipulated into feeling sorry for her.

I wanted to leave, but I was afraid God would be mad at me for leaving Tammy. I had no work coming in to get away for a while during the day. Tammy had no money coming in either. It would be a month before she received 65% of her pay from her long-term insurance she had taken out at work. I decided to give my house back since I had no way of paying for it, since I couldn't take care of two households with no money. I needed to make sure Tammy was ok before leaving; that's why I gave her all of my things out of my house.

Tammy slept most of the day, waking up around 4 pm, to take a shower and put on clean clothes. Her children would come over around 5 pm, leaving around 7 pm, not speaking a word to me. Linda was always giving me the look of "I'll get you one of these days." I'd just go out into the garage while her kids were there. They hated me because of what happened to Tammy.

When they visited their mother, it was my time for a break. They could help Tammy with her needs. Of course, that lasted for only one week, then we never saw much of them after that.

It was getting close to Thanksgiving. I reminded Tammy I wanted to drive us to Iowa for the holiday to spend it with my sister who I've not seen since we went up for the 4th of July.

I needed to see her after all that I'd been through with the shooting and all.

At first, Tammy was ok with it. But a few days before we were going to leave, Tammy changed her mind. Just another letdown. Seems like one after another since I have known her. I wanted to leave Tammy here and go to Iowa alone, but who'd watch over her? I was the only one taking care of Tammy. I couldn't leave her. I called my sister and canceled my trip.

We had Thanksgiving at Tammy's mother's house in Sapulpa, Oklahoma. Her kids were going to be there also, along with her friend Lucy who stopped over to see Tammy. This was the first time I'd met Tammy's sister. Tammy warned about her sister being the odd one in the family. I was told by Tammy to stay away from her sister. "She sleeps with everyone," Tammy said, "she will try to get you into bed if you let her." Tammy said she was crazy due to too many drugs when she was younger.

Tammy's sister seemed normal to me; we got along just fine. I think Tammy was jealous of her sister. Seemed like talking bad about family and friends ran deep with Tammy and Linda. They never had anything good to say about anyone, at any time. The apple doesn't fall far from the tree.

CHAPTER 47

Linda's Car

Linda had her car parked out at her Grandma's house because it would overheat. Edward told Linda it was not worth fixing and to buy another car instead.

"Linda, do you want Jim to look at it?" Tammy asked.

With a shitty attitude, Linda said, "No, Dad already looked at it, he said it wasn't worth fixing."

I went out for a smoke. I looked at Linda's car. "Nice car," I thought to myself, "I'll check it out. If I can fix it cheap, I'll offer Linda some money for it and give it to my daughter, Paige. She needs a car right now."

"Linda, if I could have the keys to take a look at it," I requested, "I might want to buy it from you."

Linda gave me the keys, and I went out and started the car. I saw the radiator was leaking, causing it to overheat. "Easy fix," I thought to myself. "I can fix that for less than a hundred-dollar bill."

I went into the house and asked Linda if she would take hundred and fifty dollars for the car. I told her I wasn't sure what was wrong with it, but I'd park it in the garage at Tammy's house and fix it when I had the time. Linda handed me the title and keys. I gave her the money, towed the car home, and put it in the garage.

The next day I ordered a radiator for the car. I had the car running by Monday afternoon. I called my daughter, Paige, to get the car I bought for her. My daughter came over that afternoon. She was very happy with the car, gave me a hug, said, "I love you, Dad," and drove it home.

"Why Paige was here?" Tammy asked.

"I fixed Linda's old car," I said, "and called Paige to come and get it, she could have it."

"What do you mean you fixed the car?" Tammy asked.

"I put a radiator and a thermostat in it. I called Paige to come and get it."

"Why didn't you fix it for Linda?" Tammy asked, "now she has to buy a new car."

"You asked Linda if she wanted me to look at it. She said no because her dad looked at it and said it wasn't worth fixing. So I looked at it. I knew I could fix it for less than a hundred dollars. I bought it from Linda to give to my daughter."

"Linda is going to be pissed," she said, "when she finds out you fixed it and gave it to your daughter."

"Maybe next time Linda will let me look at it instead of treating me like crap all the time," I said. "I bought the car from her, fair and square. I can do whatever I want with it. Since I have my truck, Jeep, and two Harley's, I didn't need the car."

My girls, Island and Paige, stopped over to see me one afternoon. It seemed Paige told Island I looked sad and unhappy when she came to get the car from me.

"Dad," my girls said, "you don't look good. You look tired and unhappy here. We want you to leave Tammy and go back to your house. We never get to see you anymore since you met her. Dad, you haven't seen your grandchildren since May."

"I know, girls," I said with watery eyes. "I miss my family so much, but I just can't leave Tammy right now. Who would take care of her?"

"Let Tammy's kids take care of her, Dad; you've done enough for her. She almost got you killed, Dad, and now she's taking up all your time. Please, dad, just get your things and leave, you're not happy here."

I couldn't tell my girls I was losing my house. I was embarrassed and ashamed I let myself get this far in the hole, because of a pretty face and false promises. I wanted to leave with my girls, but I had unfinished business here, I needed to get the money I spent fixing up Tammy's house before I could make any further plans to leave.

"Girls," I said. "I have some things to finish around here before I can leave. I promise you, I'll leave soon. Just let me take care of a few things first, ok?"

My girls weren't happy about me staying. I think they came over to help me pack up my things. I hugged my girls and told them both I loved them very much. It was a very sad moment for me, I had to put off my children needs for Tammy's.

Back inside the house, Tammy wanted to know what I was talking about with my daughters that took so long.

"They were just catching me up on my grandchildren, that's all." I went out into the garage for a little alone time. I sat there playing back everything my girls said to me. They were right; I haven't seen much of them since meeting Tammy. I was playing "let's catch Billy instead."

CHAPTER 48

Broken Promise

Thanksgiving was long gone, and Tammy was ready to put her tree up for Christmas. Tammy invited her kids over, as they do it together every year. I kept working on the house while they did the tree. I was in the master bathroom hanging pull ropes over the toilet so Tammy could transfer herself without any help from anyone.

I watched Tammy one day as she tried to transfer with her board, only to fail every time until I picked Tammy up and sat her on the toilet. "It was too slippery," she said. Sliding on the toilet seat, she'd almost fall out of her wheelchair. One day while Tammy was sleeping, I got into her chair and wheeled myself into the bathroom next to the toilet. I studied how I could transfer without using that stupid board. I needed something hanging from the ceiling to lift myself out of the chair onto the toilet. With straps, she could lift herself up to sit right on the seat. I installed a set of straps that I practiced with before they were just right for Tammy to use. Now she could transfer using the straps without anyone's help.

It wasn't long after that I made the same set up for the shower. Tammy was able to grab the straps, lift herself out of the wheelchair and sit on her shower chair. My days of being trapped here were getting closer to the end. Soon Tammy would be able to do everything by herself, without anyone's help.

This worked out great. I was hoping to return to work soon; I needed to make some money. Right now Tammy could do the most important things. She just needed more practice getting in and out of bed. Once she had that down, she'd be able to take care of herself after I was gone.

Tammy was sleeping so much during the day and sitting in her chair most of the night. She had a bed sore that formed on her tail bone. It was getting bad, the size of a fifty-cent piece and a half inch deep. I called the hospital and they sent out a home nurse to look at it. She showed me how to clean it every day with saline and gave me some cream to put on it. I had to make sure it was wrapped really good so Tammy's body waste couldn't get to it. Just something else on my list of things to do every day.

I received an invitation from my son to his graduation from the Fireman's Academy. I was very excited about seeing my son live out his dream of becoming a firefighter. I'd get to see him walk up on stage and receive his diploma as he became Broken Arrow's newest firefighter. Chad worked very hard to get this position, and I was very proud of him. I watched Chad start out at 130 pounds, running and hitting the weights every day, until he reached his goal. Now he was 220 pounds, a very strong man, and ready for his first call of duty.

I told Tammy, "Friday night we were going to watch my son graduate from the academy, then dinner afterward."

Tammy said, "Good for him. What time is it going to be?"

I told her "6 pm, so be ready at 5 pm, so we can make sure we get parked and get good seats."

Friday arrived. I made sure my batteries were good on my camera, as I planned on taking a lot of pictures of my son that night. But Tammy laid in bed and wouldn't get up to attend my son's graduation.

I was so pissed; I told her it was unfair to me, "After all I've done for you, and this is how you treat me? You better call someone to come over to watch you, 'cause I'm going to see my son graduate, then I'm going out to dinner with him."

I was angry at Tammy when I left her house. I felt I was being punished for something I did in the past. I didn't want to go back there, but I didn't want God to be mad at me either. What more was I supposed to do for Tammy before my work was done there? I needed to start making plans to get away from her soon. The mental abuse from her kids, along with Tammy's lying to me all the time, was hurting me mentally.

I watched my son take the stage that night, and I was so proud of him, I used a whole roll of film of Chad receiving his diploma. After it was over, we headed out to the parking lot to our vehicles. I was half way to mine, when Chad yelled, "Hey, Dad!"

I walked back over to him with a proud look on my face. Chad looked at me, he said, "I owe it all to you, Dad," then he hugged me. I've always taught my kids a good work ethic. Do what you love and love what you do, was my motto. If you don't like your job, find one you do.

Tammy tried to play it off when I returned to her house. She had her friend Penny come over to watch over her while I was gone. It felt so good being away, even for a short break.

"How was dinner?" she asked.

"It was good; I had a great time with my family."

"I'm sorry I didn't go," she said. "I didn't want you to have to deal with me on your son's special night."

"Tammy, you keep saying we are a couple, but yet you haven't done anything with me as a couple. Has it occurred to you I also have kids and family that I'd like to see from time to time? That's what couples do. Even before you got shot, you become a hermit, not doing anything outside your house. I do all the running to the store for groceries and liquor store to buy you a box of wine every other day. All you do is lay in bed until your kids come over. You never get up and hang out with me. I feel like I'm your butler, Tammy, all I do is take orders from you."

CHAPTER 49

The New Deck

"What orders do you take from me?" Tammy asked.

"Ok, 'did you feed the dogs, Jim?' 'Did you wash my bed pads, Jim?' 'Can you get me more wine, Jim, so I can take my pills?' 'Did you water my plants, Jim?' 'Did you feed the bird and clean out his cage, Jim?' 'What are you cooking tonight, Jim?' Those are just a few of the things you ask every day when you open your eyes, Tammy. Plus, I cath you every two hours to keep you dry. While you sleep, I change your bed pads when you soil them, and then I clean you up."

"I'm sorry, I didn't realize," she said, "I was asking you to do so much."

"Tammy, I have things to do every day. I work on the house while you are sleeping. I try to keep it quiet, not waking you. I mow the lawn, water your plants in the yard, all while checking on you every hour, waiting for you to wake up for a little adult conversation."

"I wished I could do my planting like I used to," she said. "I'd love to sit outside in the sun and do some repotting, but

I can't wheel myself outside because of the steps. Can you build me a ramp out the back door?"

"That just gave me an idea, Tammy," I said. "Follow me into the kitchen, let's look at something together." I opened the door to the back yard and pushed Tammy outside so we could hang out on the patio together. I started a fire in the pit, poured her a glass of wine, and handed her the poker, so she could poke the logs to keep the fire going. We just sat out there and enjoyed each other's company.

"Tammy, what do you think about me building you a deck from the doorway all the way down to the bedroom window?" I got up and walked it off for her. "It would be about twenty-five feet long. I'd come out ten feet from the house. You could roll out the door in your wheelchair, spending all day doing your repotting, or just spend the day outside in the sun. How would you like that?" I asked.

"Could you build that for me?" she asked. "I would love that, Jim. I could do what I love doing all day if I wanted to. Edward always said it would cost too much when I asked him about a deck. How much would it cost me to build Jim?"

"Around $2,500.00 to build it, but that's just materials," I said. "Of course, since you know the carpenter, we can work out a deal."

"When can you start?" Tammy asked.

"I can get materials tomorrow, start setting posts, and build the frame in one day. Tammy, the only things you can't do anymore are run and stand. But you can do everything else. Your chair is your legs now, so you are mobile. Plus, you can use your hands. I'll build you this deck if you promise to spend less time in bed. If this gives you a reason to wake up in the mornings, then I'll build it."

"I promise not to spend so much time in bed," she said, "if you build me a deck."

"It's getting late, let's call it a night, Tammy. I'll pick up supplies in the morning while you are sleeping. So just lay in bed, until I return."

She said, "Ok."

Getting her set up to be able to take care of herself and have something to do during the days after she woke up was part of my plan to get away.

Somehow, I had to break Tammy from watching prison shows every night while she laid in bed. This was driving me crazy.

"Why are we watching these prison shows every night?" I asked.

Tammy told me she wanted to see what Billy would be going through while he was in prison!

I felt like Tammy wanted to visit Billy. Why was he was always on her mind, even after he shot her, putting her in a wheelchair for the rest of her life? I didn't think she was ever going to get over Billy. He controlled her for a long time. Billy made all the rules in their relationship, and she followed them.

I had a friend who worked for the Broken Arrow Police Department. I was told the reason they didn't do anything when we called the police was because Tammy would always get Billy off by dropping the charges. So after last year when she dropped the gun charge, that made the Police Department look bad. From that day on, they wouldn't help her when she called them because Tammy would just get Billy off again. That was crazy to hear, because I was in the middle of their love-hate relationship, I could have died that day.

I was starting to find out more things Tammy hadn't told me about her and Billy. Now I know why I was alone in catching Billy. Tammy was protecting him from the police all the time; even the police figured out it was a game between the two.

I started on the deck for Tammy. It was going to be big and beautiful. The first day I set the posts in cement and wrapped the frame around the posts. I would start laying up the floor in the morning. The weather was nice for December, almost 60 degrees, but I only needed two days to build her deck.

The next day, I started laying up the floor to the deck; I was using screws to make sure it lasted a long time. I decided to make it twelve-foot-wide instead of ten foot. It was perfect. Now there was enough room for my patio furniture, my grill, and room for Tammy's planting stuff.

Tammy came rolling out after I'd laid up the flooring past the doorway. She just loved her new deck! She rolled up and down, saying how she was going to be outside.

"I have always wanted a deck," she said. "This is beautiful, Jim. Thank you so much, I love it. Now I can sit out and get some sun this summer."

Right then I thought, "Oh God, I hope she gets a new bathing suit; the one she has is nasty looking."

I finished up the deck the next day. I built her railing and even threw in a 16-foot ramp into the yard, just in case she wanted to lay out in the grass or water the plants around the house. I moved the patio furniture from my house up on the deck, along with my grill. It was perfect for entertaining or a place to get away for some quiet time.

December 4th was Tammy's birthday: I made plans a couple days before her birthday to take her out to eat. It would be her first time out in public in her wheelchair. She needed to get out of her house, back into society, for dinner.

Linda called that afternoon. She told Tammy she had invited some friends over tonight for Tammy's birthday. My plans with Tammy were overruled by Linda's announcement. We were not going out for dinner. Instead, Tammy told me to grill out some burgers for her friends who were coming over for her party that night.

I was left out of Tammy's party. That night Linda and Tammy's girlfriends sat in the kitchen, celebrating Tammy's birthday by eating cake and singing. Linda finally got one over on me; now she had bragging rights.

Christmas was only three weeks away, and Tammy wanted to do some shopping. She had done most of it online, but she wanted to go to Walmart for the first time since being sentenced to her wheelchair. I think she was ready to get out since building that deck brought her out of the house again. Tammy was ready to get back out into society once again.

I took Tammy shopping at Walmart. She just took off in her chair, while I followed pushing the cart. She did just fine, being back out in public for the first time in months. She was shopping for new clothes to wear to court, which would soon be coming after the Christmas break.

CHAPTER 50

Tulsa's Big Ice Storm

On December 10th I heard again what I thought were gunshots. I sat up in the bed and listened to what sounded like a gunfight outside her bedroom window. "What the hell is wrong with this neighborhood?" I asked out loud as I jumped out of bed to peek out the window to see who was doing all the shooting.

"Oh my God," I said as I looked out of the window. The trees were snapping and popping like bullets being shot from a gun. The ice must have been an inch thick, pulling trees to the ground, snapping them off at the trunk. We had a tree laying across the privacy fence out back. I could hear trees popping all around the neighborhood, pulling power lines down with them. We didn't have any power.

As I made my way through the dark house into the kitchen to make some coffee, I remembered we didn't have power. "Ok, I need some coffee," I was thinking to myself. How am I going to boil some water? The stove and microwave were both electric. I walked around thinking, how was I going to boil water to make me some coffee?

I'd start a fire in the fireplace! I had some wood in the garage from the work I was doing on Tammy's house. But I needed some logs to heat the house also. I went out into the garage and gathered up some small pieces of wood to start a fire until I could return with some logs from the side of the house where Tammy kept them.

I looked at the door going out to the side yard where she kept the firewood. Opening this door again this early in the morning gave me the creeps, even though Billy was in jail. I still grabbed a hammer for protection. I slowly unlocked the door and pulled it open quickly as I raised my hammer for protection, in case someone was there again.

Everything was ice covered. I took the hammer for breaking the ice off the logs so I could get to the dry ones in the middle of the pile to keep the fire going. I brought all the logs into the garage, even the wet ones, so they would dry out in time. Things were ok for a while. I kept the fire burning hot. I was able to use an old pan of Tammy's to boil some water for coffee. I poured it through the filter twice to make a pot of good hot coffee. Now that I'd some coffee in me, I could start doing my everyday chores.

I went out to my truck, using it to charge my phone and listen to the news, trying to get an update on how long the power would be out. They said power would be out up to a week or two for some places in Oklahoma! I knew we wouldn't have power for a couple of days. I needed to keep Tammy warm. I couldn't take the chance of her getting sick. I put some extra blankets on her and told her to stay in bed and keep warm until I could figure things out.

I sat in the living room on the couch watching the fire burning. It was dark in the house. The only light was from the fireplace. I felt trapped again! I couldn't work on the house; no television, no radio, I had nothing. It would be this way for a few days until the power came back on. I was getting depressed; I felt helpless, and I wanted to die! I asked God over and over, "Why was this happening to me?" I was thinking to myself, "If I still had that gun Edward gave me, I would use it right now." I was looking for a way out! I couldn't take any more of this.

I was the good guy in this story!

After sitting a couple of hours in front of the fire, I decided to get a legal pad and write this story from beginning to end. I would write it every day and keep it hidden from Tammy. This was my story! This was what I lived through, even though it's not over. But someday I would look back on this and thank God for giving me another assignment.

Tammy laid in her bed most of the day to keep warm. She needed her bed pad changed and needed to be cleaned up. I knew the water heater was gas and we could shower if needed. I got Tammy out of bed. I carried her to the shower chair after warming up the water. I made sure the door to the bathroom was closed, to keep the heat and steam inside. It was very dark inside the bathroom and even darker with the steam filling the cold room.

After Tammy had taken a shower, I made sure she had warm clothes to put on. She wanted to sit in her wheelchair in front of the fireplace. That night as we sat in front of the fireplace, Tammy sipped on her jug of wine, and I was on my second pot of coffee.

She asked, "What's for dinner?"

"I have no idea, let me see what you have in the freezer," I said. "I'm sure I can find something to cook in the fireplace."

In the freezer was a family Lasagna frozen in a foil pan. "I found something," I said. I took it in the living room to show

Tammy what we were having for dinner.

"How are you going to cook that?' she asked, "we don't have electricity."

I opened the box and slid out the lasagna, laying it on top of red hot logs as I looked at her with a smile on my face.

"You're a genius," she said.

"This is how we are going to eat for a couple of days, Tammy," I said.

Tammy's daughter Linda called around 6 pm while our dinner was cooking in the fireplace. Linda called to make sure Tammy was warm and wanted to know if everything was ok. Linda told Tammy they were in a motel with their dad. He lost power at his house. "Dad said he wasn't going to live in a dark, cold house. Dad rented a room for a week unless the power comes on sooner."

Tammy told Linda we were fine. "I took a hot shower and Jim is cooking us dinner in the fireplace just like two cowboys. We are having lasagna tonight," she said with a laugh.

While Tammy was talking on the phone with Linda, I went into the kitchen. I grabbed a cookie sheet, buttered some bread and covered it with garlic salt, placing it next the lasagna on the fire. I just love garlic toast with lasagna, and she would too I bet.

Around 8 pm we started eating lasagna and garlic toast for dinner. Of course, what was on the bottom of the pan would stay there, being charred from the flame coming from the logs. But it was a nice dinner. I enjoyed the adult conversation the most. Something I hadn't had in a long time since I was by myself most of the time while Tammy slept.

After dinner, Tammy brought up Billy's family and how they might try something since Billy was in jail now. "Mike would be the one to do something," she said, "because he is dying of cancer. He has nothing to lose. Mike would sneak up behind you with a knife. His family lives down south in the Talaimena Mountains.

"They have their own little compound. Every time we'd go there, they'd dress up in camouflage and have hunting games. They'd practice in case the law or someone else showed up. They could hide a body easily," she said. "Billy showed me what they would do if they needed to hide a body."

She told me both his parents were in prison for robbing a bank years ago. Everyone in their family is mean to the core. "But they all liked me, so I never feared going to their camp, I was told not to tell anyone about it. Billy would teach me to shoot guns, for protection of course."

"If I had known you knew how to shoot a gun," I said, getting pissed, "I would have given you the gun and would have just left until you came out to get me."

"I'm not so good to go up against Billy," she said. "He's good with guns."

That was all I needed to hear since it is dark outside and dark inside the house. Why did Tammy keep talking about Billy and his family? Did she miss the adventure, or maybe she missed being controlled by Billy? When she talked about Billy and his family, she talked like they are modern day heroes, or they were the smartest people who ever lived. Was Tammy upset that I beat Billy at his own game, since they practiced so hard to catch people like me?

Now she had gotten me worried about Mike showing up since his baby brother Billy was in jail. Am I back to square one now? Back to sleeping on the stairwell, or hiding in the bushes across the street?

I never brought up Billy to Tammy, or to anyone else; it's over now! I did my assignment from God. I took Billy off the streets, risking my life, not only for Tammy but the entire neighborhood. Billy was no longer a threat to society.

For the next few days, we were still without power. I was doing everything I could to keep my mind occupied from falling back into a depression. I started cutting up the tree that had fallen over on the fence. We needed more firewood. I burned almost everything she had.

I wrote more when I took long breaks to come inside and warm up. I still cathed Tammy every two hours. This was an everyday thing, as well as changing her bed pads two or three times a day. Since we still didn't have power in the house, I took Tammy's bed pads upstairs and washed them out in the tub; then I'd hang them in the garage to dry. Makes a person think back before they had electricity how they got by, and I was doing just that.

I started putting her son Steven's things into boxes like Tammy had asked me to. She wanted to me to finish his room and put my antique bed up there for visitors who spent the night. As soon as the power came back on, I was going to finish Steven's old bedroom so I could move to the next project. Finishing one room at a time was my plan.

I told Tammy I had all Steven's things packed up in boxes for him to pick up.

"I'll tell Steven to come and get his things," she said, "as soon as the power is back on."

"Ok, good, I will start painting his room soon but will put his boxes in the closet until he comes to get them. This way I can put my old antique bed in there. It's been sitting in the garage for some time now."

I worked on Steven's old bedroom for a couple of days, patching walls and painting when I could. It was too cold up there to do very much.

The third day without power, I was outside cutting up more of the tree which had fallen onto the fence. It was like something tapped me on the shoulder to get my attention! I stopped cutting I looked over at her porch light and it was on. I sat my chainsaw down and ran back inside the house to see lights again. This was almost the happiest day of my life; the heat was on! I could watch television and cook meals on the stove. No more cutting firewood! I could keep working on the house. What a relief it was just having electricity again.

I went into the bedroom. With cheer in my voice, I told Tammy we had power. I was like a child waking up on Christmas morning. Soon the house would be warm, and I could take off some clothes. The first thing I wanted to do was watch some television; something to occupy my mind for a while.

I started a load of bed pads and made a fresh pot of coffee. I turned on the television in time for Jeopardy. I loved using my mind. Sometimes I would surprise myself knowing more than one answer on Jeopardy. I sat back on my big green couch and watched for a full thirty minutes with a hot, fresh cup of coffee in my hands.

Tammy laid in her bed watching whatever she wanted. I gave her the remote and told her I'd be doing laundry.

Things were almost back to normal. Tomorrow I'd finish Steven's old bedroom, leaving me with two more bedrooms to finish. Then maybe I'd have some calls for some work!

CHAPTER 51

The Money Owed

That following weekend, Tammy's kids came over to visit for a while.

Tammy told Steven his things were packed up in boxes. She asked if he could take them when he left. He was pissed, cursing about his stuff being in boxes. "What do you mean, my stuff is in boxes?"

"I asked Jim to put your things in boxes for you," she said.

"He just threw my stuff in boxes!" Then Steven started saying shit to me about what I had done. He put up his fists and wanted to fight me for doing what Tammy had asked me to do.

I started walking towards him and said, "Steven, you better think about it, boy, before you stand up to me. I'm not Billy; I'll hurt your ass!"

I was ready to knock his block off. I've been through enough crap from Tammy's children and her so-called friends. I had some frustrations inside of me I'd love to get rid of right now.

"Let's see what you got, boy," I said as I was pushing Tammy away from Steven. I was ready to hurt him! All I needed was a reason, and it wouldn't take much.

Tammy told Steven to stop it as she wheeled between us, putting her hands on both of us. "I asked Jim to put your things in those boxes. Steven, you need to leave my house now! This is why I asked you to move out; you have anger problems. I cannot deal with it anymore. Please leave now!"

Steven left mad. He punched a dent into the side of my trailer as he walked past it going to his car.

Tammy apologized to me for the way Steven was acting. "I don't know what's gotten into him. He just has so much anger towards everyone like Billy did."

"Tammy, I'm tired. I'm not sure how much more of this fighting with your kids I can take. You have the most dysfunctional family I've ever seen. For the life of me, I cannot figure out why everyone is on my case. I wasn't the one who shot you and put you in that wheelchair!"

"My children told me this wouldn't have happened if we didn't meet," she said. They're mad you never left when Billy tried to run you off."

"You're right about that. You'd probably be dead, or still playing your games with Billy. Besides, you brought me into this relationship via email. You assured me I was safe when Billy started doing things, even begged me to stay. I thought you meant it, that's why I stayed."

"I'm sorry for everything, Jim."

"Tammy, I don't want to come between you and your kids, I just want them to respect me while I'm here taking care of you. Believe me, they don't want to take care of you like I do every day. One more thing, Tammy, if your son Steven puts another dent in my trailer like he did when he left, you won't stop me next time from hurting him."

"He put a dent in your trailer? When did he do that?"

"When you asked him to leave. I watched him on the camera as I was headed out to the garage for a smoke to calm down."

She said, "I'm going call Edward about what Steven did today. Steven will apologize to you for that, or he will not be welcome back over."

Things were quiet for a few days. I was able to finish Steven's old bedroom. My iron bed looked great in the room, a perfect place for me to hide away and do some writing or take a nap when needed. I hid this story between the mattress and box spring of the bed. I knew it would never be found there because Tammy couldn't go upstairs unless I carried her.

It was too cold for Tammy to sit out on her new patio, so she'd hang out on her computer most of the day. She was able to do her things, and I was able to finish the work on her house.

She never told me if she has received her insurance check. I have been waiting for the money I spent on her house while she was in the hospital. She told me I would get my money back when the check came in. It's been almost two months now.

That night as we were eating a dinner, I had prepared for us I mentioned the insurance check to Tammy.

"Tammy, have you received the insurance check on the house yet?"

"Yes, I have," she said. "I received it last month. The $12,000.00 was put into my account."

"You told me when you received it I would get my money back I used to fix your house."

"Yes I did, but we are a couple now. The money belongs to us. Do you need some money?"

"Well, I'd like the amount of money I used out of my pocket to fix this place up. I have all the receipts if you would like to see them. It doesn't matter if we are a couple or not, we aren't a married couple, Tammy. I need my money back. Please, I have bills to pay. I've lost my house over all of this crap. I have bills due, Tammy."

"I only have $2600.00 left in my account," she said, "but I will give it to you if you need it to pay your bills."

"What the hell did you do with all that money, Tammy? Did you spend my money? That's not right, Tammy. You told me I'd get my money back once you received the insurance check. Where did the money go?"

Tammy said, "I gave Linda $5000.00 to get a car, I paid my bills, and I bought Christmas presents for my family."

"I cannot believe you spent all that money without giving me my money back, the money I used to remodel your house! How could you lie to me again after what I've done for you? I trusted you, Tammy, only to be lied to again. You only told me what I wanted to hear. You never planned on giving me that money, did you? Now I have nothing, I can't even buy my family anything for Christmas or pay my bills."

Tammy was mad, or embarrassed when I confronted her about her promise to me.

"Fine, I will write you a check for the $6000.00 right now," she said.

"That's good Tammy, write me a bad check. You managed to give Billy $10,000.00 to get out of trouble with the law. But when I remodel your house after Billy shot it up, I get nothing for my efforts. And you use 'we are a couple' to get out of paying me back."

I was furious at Tammy. I'd lost everything. I found myself trapped in her house again. I had no other resources. I had to stay with her for now, taking the abuse from her kids.

I started spending more time in the garage smoking and talking to God about a way out of this. Since meeting Tammy, I'd lost my beautiful home, and I have no work coming in. I'm down to a couple of hundred dollars in the bank. Everything up to now has been lies. Tammy has lied to me from our first hello. She was punishing me for sending Billy away; I broke up their game.

During the week of Christmas, I left Tammy's house and stayed with my sister for a week. I needed a break from Tammy and her children. I had some thinking to do. I was embarrassed I let myself be used and treated like crap. I was taken full advantage of by Tammy. She used me to get what she wanted. What she wanted was to get back at me, for sending Billy to prison.

I returned New Year's Day, after my little break from the drama. I figured her kids and friends would treat me like crap if I stayed while they open presents with them. There was nothing under the tree for me anyway, after everything I had done for Tammy and her family. That was all the thanks I needed to make my plans for leaving for good.

I had asked a neighborhood girl to watch over Tammy while I was gone for the week. The neighbor girl worked as a CNA at the hospital. I knew she could take care of Tammy's bed sore, and she knew how to cath Tammy.

Tammy told me the neighbor girl was always trying to kiss her. "She would sleep in the bed with me, she was always touching me, and I felt uncomfortable with her being here."

I said, "I'm sorry she did that, Tammy, but I had no one else who knew how to clean your bed sore or do the other things I was doing for you."

The neighbor girl was not happy I came back to take over her duties. She was hard to get rid of. I could see she was on a mission to get rid of me for good, and it probably would have worked if Tammy didn't feel so uncomfortable with her. She started playing Linda against me, giving Linda more fire-power to make my life even more miserable.

CHAPTER 52

Sex Club

The sheriff delivered a couple of letters for us to appear in court. The Assistant District Attorney wanted to meet with us before the hearing started. Doug wanted to go over the case against Billy Wolf.

Tammy was worried about seeing the DA and what he might ask or say to her.

I told Tammy to tell the truth and things will be all right. I was ready to get this over with and move on with my life.

I loaded Tammy up in my truck as we headed for the DA's office to talk about the case. The drive there was quiet; Tammy didn't talk much at all. I could see she was in deep thought over what he would be asking her about Billy. I wondered if she would try and drop charges this time or would she tell the truth? How would she act after seeing Billy in court?

We arrived at the courthouse and made our way up to the DA's office. We waited outside his office until he came out. He asked to see Tammy first. I sat there looking at a magazine. I also kept my ears open, hoping I could hear some talking going on in the office.

Tammy came out after about an hour; her eyes were red she had been crying. I suppose it would be hard for her talking about the shooting again.

It was my turn, and I jumped up with pep in my step. I shook the DA's hand as we met at the doorway of his office. Finally, I'd get my chance to tell someone who cared the real story of how Billy Wolf tried to kill me. I wanted to make sure Billy never saw daylight outside a prison wall again.

Doug said, "Have a seat, Jim," as he pointed to the chair across from his. "I'd like to go over with you how we are going to prosecute Billy Wolf. I need to get all the facts of what happened that day so we can build our case against Billy."

"Yes sir," I said, "ask anything you want."

"Did you notice a gym bag at the door where Billy held a gun to your head?" he asked.

"I was only looking into the barrel of the gun," I said. "I didn't get a chance to look around. I saw Billy's black eyes staring at me and the gun. That's all I saw."

"Billy had a big gym bag at the door," he said. "What we found inside of it were nude photos of Tammy, KY Jelly, and some sex toys, with a lot of bullets."

I just looked at Doug with a confused look on my face. I knew Billy was weird from what I heard from Devonna, but this took the cake.

"Billy had sex toys, and nude pictures of Tammy?" I asked.

"You don't know anything about this, do you?" he asked. He could see the disgust on my face.

"No, I don't know anything about what Billy had, or what he did with Tammy before I came into the picture," I said.

"Tammy and Billy would attend a sex club quite often," he said. "Did you know that?"

"No sir," I said, "what is a sex club?"

"They would go to a sex club and let people watch them have sex through a big glass window," he said, "while they sat at a table with a drink."

I couldn't believe my ears. Not Tammy; she wouldn't do anything like that. She has never mentioned anything like that to me.

"Where is this club you are talking about?" I asked. "Is it here in Tulsa?"

"It's off of 21st and Sheridan," he said, "in a little strip center that has plywood over the windows with no name out front."

"Oh my God," I said. "I had no idea about any sex clubs, or what Tammy and Billy did during their relationship. This information about Tammy gives me a different light on what 's been going on the whole time since meeting Tammy."

"I can see you don't know anything about this," he said. "I'm sorry that I had to bring it to your attention."

"I'm glad you brought this up, Doug, because Tammy would have never told me about the disgusting things she was doing with Billy. She could have given me something, or maybe she already has?"

"Billy's intentions were to kill you in front of Tammy," he said, "then take her away. I don't know where he was going to take her. By you getting away from Billy ruined his plans and his day. I can promise you Billy will be going away for a long time. Right now we are charging him with six counts of attempted murder, and we're pushing for a life sentence for each count.

"How are you doing, Jim?" he asked, as he looked at me with sympathy in his eyes, feeling sorry for the innocent man in all this.

"I've been better. Some days are harder than others, but I'll manage to keep my chin up, moving forward from all of this."

I stood up and shook Doug's hand. I felt like I had a friend in Doug. He seemed to care about my wellbeing and not just the case against Billy.

From that day forward I looked at Tammy differently. Tammy and Billy were just a modern-day Bonnie and Clyde. Tammy was using men as her little toys, until Billy begged her back, or forced his way in with his little scams. And the sex club! I couldn't wait to find out what her excuses are for going.

I walked out of Doug's office. Tammy looked at my eyes. She could see I was told about the little games she and Billy's were playing. The same thing Doug brought up to her attention. Now I was thinking, "Maybe I should walk past Tammy drive back to her house to pack my things and leave." But I smiled at her. I wanted answers. I would get them as soon as we were home.

"Are you ready to go home, Tammy?" I asked.

"Yes," she said with a smile, sinking into her chair like a whipped puppy.

Tammy knew Doug would tell me everything. That's why she was crying in his office. How could Tammy possibly think she could hide this from me and no one would be the wiser?

This whole time Tammy was blaming everything on Billy when she was behind it.

I kept my composure all the way back to Tammy's house. I didn't want to start something while driving. My plans were to lay her in the bed, get her a glass of wine, sit in a chair at the bottom of the bed, then bring up what I had just learned today about her disgusting life before me. Why did she keep it from me? Why did she involve me?

I was in shock! How could this be the beautiful woman I'd met at a roadside nursery, just a few months ago, be completely different than what she appeared to be? On the day we met, I thought Tammy was so perfect and so innocent. I even thanked God for bringing her into my life. Except, she was hiding her secret life behind her looks to lure me in to her world of lies and drama with Billy. She only told me what she wanted me to hear so I'd stay with her.

I laid Tammy in her bed and poured her a glass of wine. Truth serum, if she had enough. I pulled my wing back chair up to the end of the bed.

"Tammy, I found out some things about you today," I said, "which came as a surprised me."

"What did you hear?" she asked.

"I think you know what I'm going to tell you, Tammy. Does sex club ring a bell?"

"Yes it does," she said. "Billy has taken me there, but only two times."

"First of all, Tammy, I've never heard of a sex club, but that doesn't have anything to do with me knowing or not. Why did you go?"

"Billy took me. I didn't want to go, but he talked me into it."

"I figured as much, Tammy; you would blame it on Billy since he is not here to defend himself. You have a mind of your own, right? Can I presume Billy held a gun to your head and forced you to go?"

"No, Billy didn't hold a gun to my head. He just kept asking until I finally gave in. I didn't like it. I never wanted to go back, but Billy would force me."

"But you did go back! So, let me get this straight, you'd have sex in this room, while people watched you through a glass window?"

"Yes, we would go into this glass room, which had a bed in it. We could see out into the crowd as they just sat and watched us have sex with each other."

"Did it make you feel like a movie star, Tammy? I bet it did. You were getting all this attention. All you had to do was perform well. Was it just you and Billy, or were there others joining in?"

"Only one time Billy brought another man in with us."

"So, Billy brought another guy to have sex with you and him?"

"Billy just picked a guy out of the crowd to join us."

"I cannot believe you, Tammy. You could have given me some sexually transmitted disease, or maybe you already have. I don't know!"

"All I have is herpes, Jim, and I'm taking medication for it. I told you that."

"Yes, you told me. I forgot you told me the truth once. I remember Billy had a cold sore, that's how you got herpes. You assured me I couldn't get it since you were on medications. Is that true, or not?"

"You're fine Jim," she promised.

"You just told me you had been there only two times. Ok, Tammy let's start telling the truth now because you haven't been telling me the truth from day one. All this time you made me think Billy was the bad person in your relationship; that you were the good catch, the perfect woman. And I believed you."

"I haven't lied to you," she said. "What have I lied to you about?"

"Tammy, this whole relationship with you, has been filled with lies from the first night you stayed at my house. You only told me what you wanted me to hear about Billy, so you could have the attention you require. Not once did you tell me I'd be in any kind of danger or that my vehicles would be damaged. You kept me here so Billy and I would fight over you, another part of your attention seeking games. And you almost got me killed over it.

"Now how many times have you been to that club?" I asked. "The truth, Tammy."

"Three or four times," she said. "Once my friend came down from Florida with her boyfriend. Billy and I took them to the club."

"You took your friend who came to visit to the club?" I asked. "What the hell is wrong with you?"

"Billy wanted me to ask them to go," she said. "I told her about it before they got here. They wanted to go with us."

241

"I don't know what to think Tammy. I think you had no intentions of finding a good man to be with. You used me to get attention from Billy until I left. I was the honest one in this. I thought you loved me, but you loved the attention I was giving you, that's all."

I walked out of the bedroom shaking my head because it hurt. I slipped out into the garage to have a smoke. I was trying to sort through what I was told about the woman who I once thought I would spend my life with. It's crazy how things seem to unfold when you are hiding the truth.

"How much more time here, God, before my work is done?" I asked. God does work in mysterious ways; he has his way of communicating with me.

I sat on a stool in the garage smoking. The sun at that moment hit the door just right, where I could see sunlight coming from under it. I got off the stool and kneeled down on the floor to look at how much gap was under the door Billy was standing at that morning. I couldn't believe my eyes, there was at least a half inch gap under that door. I could have seen Billy standing out there if I would have looked under the door. I had no idea there was such a big gap there. I could have seen Billy's boots that morning, gone back into the house, and gotten Tammy and Lori out down the street to a safe place while calling the police to get Billy.

I could finally see the light at the end of the tunnel. I knew my days with Tammy would soon end. I would finish my job here, making sure she was ok and had everything she needed to carry on with her life without me.

CHAPTER 53

Selling my Harley

I'd act as if everything is fine and finish my work here. Although, I wouldn't just leave without telling Tammy. I had made arrangements with a friend of mine to buy my 1999 Harley Ultra for $9500.00 so I'd have some cash to start my new life since I wasn't going to receive any of the $6000.00 from Tammy. I needed to sell something to be able to move on. It was just another loss this relationship which has cost me big time

Things went on as usual; Tammy sat at her computer for hours. I found things to keep me occupied. I spent a lot of time in the garage packing some things quietly that I wasn't leaving with Tammy, storing them in my trailer. I didn't want anyone to see what I was doing, so I'd load things in my trailer during the morning hours while Tammy was sleeping.

Tammy called me into the house one afternoon. She had something to show me on her computer. She was all happy and giggly about something.

"Look at this, Jim," she said. "I was reading a story about this woman who had a skiing accident which left her paralyzed from the waist down like me. She met a man, they got married, and they had a baby together."

"Good for her," I said. "There is love out there for everyone."

Tammy asked, "What do you think about us having a baby? I could stop the pill, and we could have a baby. We'd have to hurry though, 'cause I'm getting older. Not sure how many eggs I have left."

"I don't know if that's such a good idea, Tammy," I said. "I think having a baby would just make things worse with your kids. They don't like me as it is. I'd hate to see how they'd treat a baby from me."

Talking about having a baby was not what I wanted to hear from Tammy. I'd let her ride this out, maybe she would find something else to pursue. Something for her to do while she is in her wheelchair. She was spending the day reading about people who overcame their disability, using it to their advantage. This was a good thing; she needed that after I was gone for good.

Tammy got all hyped up on the baby thing. She talked about it for the rest of the night. I was going to make sure we didn't have sex. I wasn't going to take any chances of being trapped here. It had been three months since we had had sex, the day I brought her home for a visit was the last time. I swore to myself then I'd never do that again! I made up every excuse I could up until now. I was running out of excuses, and Tammy was getting wise to them. Since the work on the house was done, I had no more excuses. Tonight I had to be intimate with Tammy to keep things from being revealed about my true plans. I'm bad about keeping things away from people. I can't lie, my face was a dead giveaway at times. That was my weakness.

A couple days later, my friend showed up to purchase my bike. Tammy answered the door that day.

"Hello," she said.

"Is Jim here?" he asked.

Tammy yelled for me, saying, "Someone is at the door for you."

"Hey," I said, "how are you doing? Come out to the garage with me."

He followed me to the garage and looked at my bike. My Ultra Glide was a champagne color with black flames. A beautiful bike, it was worth every penny I was asking.

"That's a good-looking bike," he said. "can I hear it run?"

"Sure," I started the bike.

"Do you take cash?" he asked.

"That's my favorite kind of money," I said. "I promise you will love this bike. I bought it in Iowa last year from Mason City Harley Davidson."

We pushed the bike out to his trailer and he strapped it down. I watched him drive away with the bike and walked back into the garage with my head down. I didn't want to sell my bike or lose anything else, but I needed the money to hold me over for a while.

"Who was that?" she asked. "Why did he take your bike?"

"I sold my bike to him. He's a friend of mine from American Airlines."

"Why did you sell your bike?"

"Because I only need one bike now since you can't ride anymore. I kept my '77 Shovel and sold my '99 Ultra Classic."

"Why didn't you sell the old bike instead?"

"Because it has sentimental value to me. I hope I never have to sell that one."

"How much did you get for it?" she asked.

"He gave me $9500.00 for it."

"What are you going to do with the money?"

"Put it in my bank account to pay my bills. I told you, Tammy, I needed the money back that I used repairing your house so I could make my house payments and pay my bills which were due. Why do you ask?"

"Well, since we are a couple now living together maybe you should close your account. I'll add you to my account and get your own card. If you're on my account, then you can pay the bills with your card for me."

"No thank you," I said. "I like my bank. We'll just keep things the way they are for now. Maybe, later on, we'll do it, let's just see how things go."

Tammy said, "Ok."

I rolled that money up in a sock and hid it under the seat of my truck, tucked tightly into the seat springs. I worked hard teaching Tammy to do things herself, like getting into the shower with her straps that I hung for her. I also taught Tammy to use the straps over the toilet, and I built her a deck for play time. My time here was getting shorter every day. After court was over, I'd make plans to move on with my life. Tammy was well-taken care of with all of the things I was leaving with her.

CHAPTER 54

Court Hearings

The first day of court, and I was ready for it to begin. I'd be first to enter the courtroom to give my story. Tammy and I were waiting in the office area behind the courtroom waiting for Billy to arrive.

Behind me, I looked just in time to see the officers bringing Billy through the same area we were sitting in. Billy brushed Tammy has he walked by to get her attention and to let her know he was ok. Tammy said she was frightened that Billy touched her. She knew what it meant. I didn't believe Tammy; it was just a ploy for attention.

I went into the courtroom first and took my seat next to the judge. I swore to the Bible and God I'd tell the whole truth.

I sat there, looking over at Billy the whole time. I'd never seen Billy in person without a ski mask on, just a picture Tammy had shown me. He was dressed up in a gray suit, with his hair combed to the right side. He wore a pair of thin framed glasses. He was clean shaven too. Billy didn't look like a man who would do things with a gun, although he looked like someone sneaky who would do things behind someone's back.

The DA asked, "Mr. Edwards, do you know who the man was who held a gun to your head the morning of October 1st?"

"Yes, I do," I said. "Billy Wolf." I was looking over at Billy the whole time.

"Mr. Edwards, is Billy Wolf in this courtroom?"

"Yes, sir, he is," I said.

"Mr. Edwards, can you point to Billy Wolf for the court?"

"Yes sir," I said. "He is right over there," pointing to Billy and staring at him.

"Mr. Edwards, can you tell the court what happened the morning of October 1st?"

"Yes sir, I can. I spent the night at Tammy's house September 30th, because Tammy threw me a birthday party that night. I needed to get up early to finish a job. Tammy's daughter woke us up at 7:23 am. I jumped out of bed and told Tammy I would make some coffee. I told her I'd be right back. I started some coffee then proceeded into the garage to have a smoke when I heard some scratching at the back door of the garage. I thought it Tammy's dogs wanting in to hang out with me. I open the door, and there stood Billy Wolf dressed in black holding a gun to my head. Billy was just staring at me with his black eyes looking through the holes in the mask he was wearing. I thought I was going to die standing there. I waited for the gun to go off."

"Mr. Edwards, can you tell the court what happened next?"

"I tried closing the door on Billy, but he kept trying to push it back open while reaching in with his gun, trying to shoot me in the head. I was on my knees at the door looking up at the gun the whole time. After what seemed like a lifetime holding on the door, I heard a loud gunshot into my ear.

The door then closed. I reached up and locked the door, checking my head for blood as my ears were ringing. Then I ran back into the house to protect Tammy from Billy. I saw Billy running to the kitchen door. He kicked it in and started shooting down the hall at me."

"Mr. Edwards, did you have a gun?"

"Yes, sir! I was given a 1927 Smith and Wesson six-shooter. It was a .38 caliber. The gun was given to me by Tammy's ex-husband to protect his daughter who was living with Tammy. I had six bullets in the gun. I used them to keep Billy in the kitchen until help arrived. When I ran out of bullets, I had to leave to save my life."

Billy just sat there and listened to my story about how he failed to get me, not showing any expressions on his face.

"Mr. Edwards, that was some story. I'm sure I'm talking for everyone in here, I'm sorry you had to go through that horrible morning on October 1st.

"Mr. Edwards, is there anything else you would like to add before I ask for my next witness?"

"Just one thing, sir," I looked over at Billy Wolf. With a stern look on my face, I said, "Billy, game over!" I got up out of my chair to leave the courtroom.

I returned to the waiting room while Tammy gave her testimony to the court. I had no idea what Tammy said in the courtroom. Tammy was in love with Billy. She only halfway answered questions, trying to be easy on Billy.

Tammy was in the courtroom for two hours telling her story about what took place that morning. Tammy was on center stage again. She was getting all the attention from the court. They knew who Tammy and Billy were before and after this happened.

After today, we'd have to return several more times before it was over for good.

"Billy was giving me the 'wolf look' the whole time," she said, "I was telling the court what happened."

I was really getting tired of Tammy talking about Billy's wolf look he gave people to scare them. Tammy was full of shit; I could smell it now. Tammy could no longer fool me with her "feel sorry for me" statements. Little did Tammy know, she'd lost both Billy and I. She'd be alone from now on. After court was over, I made some plans to pack my things and move on with my life.

Sentencing day for Billy Wolf finally arrived. We had seen all the pictures from the damage Billy did to Tammy's house. We saw pictures of Tammy's dead dog laying in the bedroom on the floor. We saw it all. Today Billy would be sentenced for his crime spree. He was only being charged for the shootings and nothing else he did during that five-month span to Tammy and I.

Billy Wolf was sentenced to six life terms. He'd be eligible for parole when he turned eighty-five years old. Out in the hallway after Billy received his sentence from the jury, Billy's mother came over to Tammy. She was red faced from crying. I could see her anger. She yelled at Tammy.

Billy's mother said, "Look what you done to my son, you bitch. I'm glad you are in that wheelchair. You deserve it. I hope you die in that chair." She walked out of the courthouse crying for her son.

This is my story, about how I was lured into a love-hate relationship by a pretty face and secrets. I went through much more abuse than I have written in this story. The mental abuse from Tammy, Linda, and Lucy almost put me over the edge. There came a time when I wanted to end my own life because things were so bad there for me. I was "The Boyfriend," being blamed, and not the hero.

Devonna was right about leaving Tammy the third time. I packed up some of my sentimental things, leaving Tammy with all of my furniture and paintings I had in my beautiful home at one time. All the cash I had was the $9,500.00 from selling my Harley.

After packing up my truck and trailer with a few of my things, I woke Tammy up at 10 am. I helped her get into the shower one last time. I dressed Tammy up real pretty. I asked Tammy to meet me in the kitchen by the garage door. I had something to show her.

Tammy saw my truck and trailer facing the street.

Tammy asked, "Why are your truck and trailer facing the street? Are you going somewhere?"

"Tammy, this is hard for me to say; I asked God to put angels over you. It's time for me to go now. My job here is done. Billy is gone for good, and you have everything you need. I have a better life waiting out there for me somewhere."

Tammy yelled at me to go. "Just leave me here alone in this wheelchair!"

"Tammy, after everything which has happened to me since last May, I concluded after the abuse I suffered from everyone in your life, my job here was to take you and Billy out of society before you both hurt someone. Now neither of you can continue to hurt people with your mental games.

"Tammy, don't be mad at me. I'm sorry, I did everything I could to make this work between us. But it takes two people to have a relationship. Now, give me a hug goodbye, please!"

Tammy didn't hug me, but I gave her one. I kissed her on her forehead. She sat there in her wheelchair feeling sorry for herself.

"See you later," I said, with a nod. I walked out to my truck, feeling a state of calmness inside. I felt free now. It was over for good this time; no turning back. I looked back at Tammy one last time as I was getting into my truck. She was crying, watching me leave her for the last time.

Tammy never gave me the money for working on her house or the money for fixing her air-conditioner back in July. She never thanked me for trying to save her that morning or for anything I did for her during our time together.

As for my tooth, which was killing me, that night. I had to have it pulled. The one empty space in my mouth is a reminder of October 1st.

I never went back to Tammy's house. I deleted her number from my phone right after leaving. I started rebuilding my new life with what little I still had left. What started with an email from Tammy asking for a meeting ended with losing a year of my life rebuilding and trusting again.

I never received any medals, interviews, or parades in my honor for standing up to Billy that morning, risking my life for the girl of my dreams, who I thought after our first meeting I'd spend the rest of my life with.

I haven't been able to delete out of my mind what took place during that time in my life. The mental games Tammy played with me, keeping me around for Billy to hunt down for the personal attention Tammy craved from everyone she met.

God played a big part in this story. He delivered messages through Devonna, keeping me safe. God traded a dog's life to spare mine that morning, keeping Billy from killing me at the door. There were over 250 bullet holes inside Tammy's house. Not one of those bullets found me.

Thank you for reading my story, *The Boyfriend*.